UNANCESTRAL
VOICE

Owen Barfield

UNANCESTRAL

VOICE

WESLEYAN UNIVERSITY PRESS

Middletown, Connecticut

192
B23u
55754
Oct. '66

Library of Congress Catalog Card Number: 65-19854
Printed in the United States of America
First American Edition

Acknowledgment

*

The passages quoted from *Joseph Karo.
Lawyer and Mystic*, by R. J. Z.Werblowski,
are reproduced by kind permission of the
Clarendon Press

PART ONE

ONE

There men were talking about the recent prosecution, and acquittal, of the publishers of D. H. Lawrence's book, *Lady Chatterley's Lover*.

'The reason,' said Burgeon gloomily, 'why no one except Counsel for the Prosecution had a word to say *against* the book was simply that, for reasons best known to themselves, the Prosecution did not call any evidence. Of *course*, they could have found plenty of witnesses if they had asked for them.'

'Expert witnesses?' asked Middleton, who was neutral.

'Just as expert—if it's possible to be an expert on the subject of obscenity—as the witnesses for the Defence.'

'Perhaps the Prosecution's point was that it's *not* a matter for experts.'

'Then why didn't they argue it? The whole case was muddled, in my opinion, from start to finish. The Prosecution conceded the literary value at the outset—and yet most of the thirty-five Defence witnesses were literary men or women.'

'But surely it takes a literary man to distinguish between literature and pornography?'

'Between literature and *mere* pornography, yes. But, as I say, that point was conceded in advance. In any case, "obscene" is the word used in the Act. All the jury had to decide was whether the book is obscene or not. And it obviously is.'

'Only,' said Rodney, who was pro-Lawrence, 'if you assume that lust is obscene.'

'Well, isn't it? No one wants to stop people talking about it in a rational way. But if it's described sympathetically and in detail it's obviously disgusting.'

'I don't agree at all. The Victorians thought so, or pretended they did. That didn't prevent them from—'

'We're getting cluttered up,' interrupted Middleton, 'with a

11

lot of words—pornography, obscenity, lust, disgusting—which we are probably using with different value-judgments. Hadn't we better evaluate them ?'

'You can't evaluate disgust,' said Rodney. 'It's an immediate revulsion of feeling. Either you experience it or you don't. It depends on all sorts of things; use, for one. You can get used to anything—including four-letter words, as some of the Defence witnesses pointed out.'

'I shouldn't wonder,' said Burgeon, 'if it wasn't just that straightforward healthy revulsion that the Prosecution relied on. Mistakenly, as it turned out. Rodney's quite right—but not only about lust. Nobody's disgusted by anything today. People write with gusto—play after play, novel after novel—about every filthy thing under the sun, lavatories, sewers, torture for the fun of it, murder as an interesting experiment, rape, patricide, matricide, schoolgirls running a brothel—not to mention the sexual perversions, lesbianism, transvestism, necrophily, and of course masochism and sadism *ad lib*, and the one thing nobody ever says about them—certainly no critic ever says—is that they are disgusting.'

' "Sophisticated" is the word,' murmured Middleton.

'D. H. Lawrence himself was disgusted by quite a lot of things,' said Rodney. 'What he called "sex in the head", for instance. He would cheerfully have classified as "obscene" most of the books and plays Burgeon is thinking of.'

'All the same,' said Burgeon, 'I think he is a good deal responsible for them.'

'Why ?'

'Because he popularized the notion that reticence, as such, is a bad thing.'

'How he hated hypocrisy of any sort!'

'Exactly. He thought reticence and hypocrisy are the same thing. And that is the current cant.'

'Anyway,' put in Middleton, 'it is only reticence about lust that we are concerned with, as far as *Lady Chatterley* is concerned. Perhaps we can all agree that obscenity is some quality or other by which we *ought* to be—or by which it is a good thing to be—disgusted. If so, the only question is whether lack of reticence about lust is obscene or not.'

'What about pornography ?' said Rodney. 'Lawrence once wrote about that himself.'

12

'We can leave it out,' Burgeon said. 'It is simply obscenity in art or literature.'

'What exactly do you mean by "lust", Burgeon?' asked Rodney.

'That is easy. It is the physical element in the sexual relation abstracted from all the other elements and concentrated on for its own sake.'

'I doubt if Lawrence would have agreed with the definition. If there was one thing he hated, it was abstraction.'

'Very likely,' said Middleton, 'but I don't quite see how he could help agreeing with it. Any other element that is let in—fancy or poetry, for instance—let alone devotion—would presumably be "sex in the head".'

'That, of course,' added Burgeon, 'was precisely his dilemma, and it is the point the Prosecution ought to have seized on. But they didn't even mention it. He is bound by his doctrine to abstract the body from the rest of the personality and concentrate on it. Therefore he is bound to be obscene—that is, if we agree that descriptions of lust in action are obscene—and the fact that he also insists that obscenity is necessary and desirable is irrelevant.'

'You know,' said Rodney, 'you are being quite unfair to Lawrence. And you are unfair because everything you say is based on assumptions that he flatly denied. You should read some of his other books—*Apocalypse*, for instance—the last he wrote. He has made it clear that "the body" for him meant so much more than our separate little chunks of flesh and blood, separate from each other and separate from the cosmos. The body meant to Lawrence the whole universe, even including the sun and the planets. He thinks we have lost our link with all that by denying the body. He looks right back to the time when men thought of the heart or the liver as the seat of consciousness—not the brain. It's a magnificent vista. He describes how, with the coming of what we are pleased to call "the spirit"—which he connects with Socrates—the cosmos died. Ever since then we have been content to live in a dead or dying cosmos, hoping for some kind of heaven after our own death. He wanted to restore us to life, here and now.'

'Well, I *have* read *Apocalypse*,' said Burgeon, 'and there are certainly some fine and deep things in it. It wouldn't be Lawrence if there weren't. But what a sad hotchpotch it is! He purports to

give an account of the whole evolution of Western consciousness
—and he actually writes off Christianity—and not only Christianity, but the whole momentous Hebrew incision, from Moses
to Maccabaeus, that preceded it. Every time he touches on either
of these he simply cocks an embarrassing snook—at least, I
should have supposed his educated disciples find it embarrassing;
but it's a mad world, my masters, and perhaps they don't.

'And then what a muddle he is in! At one time he is looking
back into the "dark soul" of primitive man, dark with a kind of
Darwinian animal overtone. At another he is telling us that in
those days man lived with a life that was "like white light". The
truth is he knew almost nothing about the history of consciousness. If, when he disclosed that men used to think of the heart, or
the liver, or the blood, as the seat of consciousness, he had gone a
little farther, he would have discovered that, for that very reason,
they did *not* think of these organs as having much to do with life
or "potency"—to use one of his own favourite words. They
thought that the head, and what Homer called the "psyche"
inside it, were the seat of conscious life and that the spirit flowed
down from there into the genitals. In other words, if "potency",
and our awareness of it, is to be equated with sex, it was *they* who
suffered from "sex in the head", and to an extent that Lawrence
never even dreamed of.'

'Oh?' said Rodney. 'And what about the phallic cults? What
about Priapus?'

'Of course. I didn't say "confined" to the head. But it's
obvious, if you really go into the meanings of their words—as
Onians did in his *Origins of European Thought*—that their whole
consciousness was different. The two extremes—or rather the
currents of life in them—were linked in some way . . . there
was a bridge, which has broken down . . . united in some way I
do not understand. I only wish I did. It might well be the key to
almost everything. But that isn't at all what Lawrence says. He
wants to have it that the consciousness of early man was totally
different from our own, and also wants to have it that, E. and
O.E., it was essentially the same, only they chose to make a
different use of it.'

'That all sounds very impressive,' said Rodney, 'but if he was
really as ignorant as you make out, how do you account for the
fact that no one else seems to be aware of it? You could fill a
small library with the books that have been written about him

since his death. And have you read the Penguin on the trial—the evidence given by the witnesses for the Defence, practically all of them men with distinguished minds?'

It was Middleton who answered him:

'The cloud of witnesses? I don't see any great problem there. The ignorance of the average literary man in the twentieth century about anything that happened more than a few hundred years ago has to be dipped into to be believed. It is almost unfathomable.'

'Solemn asses,' said Burgeon. 'Solemn asses!'

'I fancy,' Rodney said rather stiffly, as he got up and knocked out his pipe, 'we are wasting our time.'

Soon after that the conversation petered out. It had been inconclusive, as no doubt many another conversation on the same topic among the more thoughtful fraction of the clerisy had been during the last few months; though it might have been otherwise if, like the jury at the Old Bailey, they had been locked up together until they had finally decided whether *Lady Chatterley's Lover* was an 'obscene article' or not.

But in spite of his last flippant comment (which he rather regretted) Burgeon was genuinely puzzled. 'Solemn asses,' he thought on his way home—well, and so they were. But how, after all, *did* one explain, not just the fuss, but the *enormous* fuss that was made about D. H. Lawrence? No doubt the tenacity of Dr. Leavis accounted for a good deal; but put it at its highest: there remained the problem of Leavis himself. What sort of *range* could a man's mind have, who believed with every fibre of his being that D.H.L. was a mighty prophet? When he reached home he turned over the pages of his copy of *Apocalypse* and one or two paragraphs caught his eye . . . 'Man wants his physical fulfilment first and foremost,' he read, 'since now, once and once only, he is in the flesh and potent.'

And again, just before he closed the book and turned out the light:

'There is nothing of me that is alone and absolute except my mind and we shall find that the mind has no existence by itself, it is only the glitter of the sun on the surface of the water . . .'

Burgeon slept.

It was next morning that the event, if it ought to be called an event, occurred; or rather the first of the series of events with which this chronicle is mainly concerned. It was still very early.

Burgeon was lying in bed. He had drunk a cup of tea, but there were still three-quarters of an hour or so before he needed to bestir himself. His body was inert and full of sleep, but his mind was very wide awake. It was also quite empty. Deliberately he decided to spend the time available to him in recollecting last night's conversation; and, as he proceeded to do so, he was surprised and rather delighted to find that both memories and thoughts presented themselves in a way which differed a good deal from the way they normally took, when his body and his mind were both equally awake. In an interesting and agreeable manner the whole conversation, or what he remembered of it, seemed to be arranging itself in patterns, although at the time it had seemed desultory and shapeless enough. This, he thought, would be a good state of mind to cultivate if one were trying to write a play. Deliberately, again, he refrained from following up this last train of thought, in order to continue concentrating on the recollection. Immediately after that it happened. At least, that was how he put it to himself afterwards, while he was shaving, but had still not yet quite shaken off the quiet of the night. Later on, he was inclined to think that that might be an altogether too sensational expression.

For what, after all, was the 'it' that happened? Since he had never told anyone about it, he had not yet made any attempt to clothe it in words. It was, however, something like this. He did *not* hear any voice. And yet a train of thought began presenting itself to him in the same mode in which thoughts present themselves when we hear them from the lips of another. They included thoughts which he himself was not aware of having ever previously entertained. For the most part the thoughts which were 'given' in this way were naked of words. He himself had to find the words before he forgot the thoughts—and in order that he might not forget them. Occasionally, however, an actual phrase or sentence came with the thought, without any effort being required on his part: *interior is anterior*, for example, and, a little later on: *the transforming agent*. If all this was surprising enough, it startled him a good deal more (but only when he came to reflect on it afterwards) that most of what reached him in this way purported to be neither speculation nor judgment but actual information on matters of fact.

Later, as we shall see, he considered the whole problem of the nature of the experience and came to terms with it. But at the

16

moment it will be more in place to record the most striking part of what came to him, in whatever way it did come, on this particular morning after that conversation about *The Trial of Lady Chatterley*.

First of all, there arose from the dim recesses of his memory four lines from an erotic medieval Latin lyric:

> *Post blanda Veneris*
> *Commercia*
> *Lassatur cerebri*
> *Substantia—*

And then, by what seemed an almost organic development from this, he discovered—became aware—was informed (put it how you will)—or he just *thought*—that he had been misjudging those witnesses for the Defence—and indeed D. H. Lawrence himself. No doubt many of them were intellectual Osrics, 'contemporary' by their own definition, and thus only venturing to think the sort of thing they mostly heard said around them. And yet (as he now saw) most of them genuinely *felt* as they spoke. Moreover, not what they said, but the fact that they had been so easy to find—that there were so many of them saying the same thing—was obviously of very great significance. Significant above all was the fact that seventy or eighty years ago you would have been hard put to find even one.

For now it was put to him that a great change had taken place, almost in his own time, in the very constitution of Western man. He was no physiologist and did not bother himself with the question whether the change was one that could be detected anatomically, though he thought it unlikely. What he did know, or what he was told, was—and clearly it also had something to do with the nature of this very experience of his—that things had been going on for the last three or four hundred years of which ordinary physiology as yet knew nothing, although they closely concerned both the brain and the reproductive organs. Man's interior—that interior which was also anterior—had been at work, as it had been at work also in the earlier stages of his existence. It had been at work, gradually developing and informing some sort of delicate structure or complex of forces in the front part of the brain and at the same time in the organs of reproduction.

17

But he knew also, or seemed to know, that it had recently finished that work; and had therefore been set free—and that was why it was even now pouring into his own consciousness, 'informing' it in the other sense of the word.

To his great annoyance at this point he was obliged, for domestic and occupational reasons, to break off. He had to get up. And it was remarkable how, as the ground took the weight of his feet, the whole experience—the train of thought that had seemed so present and so solid—although it did not actually vanish into limbo after the manner of idle reveries, departed almost at once to a remote distance.

At that distance, for many weeks, it remained. This would be a more straightforward chronicle if we could go on to tell how the next morning he was able to summon up the same interesting state of mind and continue, so to speak, from where he left off. But nothing of the sort happened. In point of fact, he thought very little more about it. For one thing he was, as lawyers mostly are, very busy. But there were other reasons, too. Whenever his mind did go back to it, and endeavour to survey its faint outline in the distance to which it had since withdrawn, he was always met by two difficulties. In the first place, what was the correct standpoint to adopt towards it? How was he to think of it? And the 'how' here did not merely signify 'in what way'. It was more difficult than that. How was he to be able to think about it at all? What was he to *call* it?—for it is difficult to think of anything for which one has no name.

The other difficulty was this. In so far as the thoughts that had come to him in that distinctive way had purported to convey information (and he recalled the information clearly enough), how should he regard it? What reliance could he place on it? How could it, for instance, be *tested*? It was this second difficulty which inclined him to disregard it altogether, simply to withdraw and take no further notice of it; and in this inclination there was even a trace of fear. Burgeon was no mystic. To trance-conditions of any sort he was a stranger and an enemy. And, while there had been for him on that occasion nothing remotely resembling a trance—indeed, he recalled that he had never felt more fully conscious and clear-headed—his profession had brought him into touch with too many people, paranoiacs in particular, who were clear-headed enough and at the same time, to say the least of it, wrong-headed. Desperately wrong-headed.

For all these reasons he did what many people have done about many similar glimpses; and that is precisely nothing. Indeed, if it had not been for a not very exciting accident which we shall relate in the next chapter, he might very well have gone on doing nothing about it for the rest of his life.

TWO

We must now attempt to describe the accident just referred to without making either too much or too little of it. Not too little, because it was, in fact, this that ultimately determined the attitude Burgeon chose to adopt towards the event recorded in the previous chapter. Not too much, because its essential connection with that event may be slight enough. It may even be non-existent. That is a matter which the reader will no doubt judge for himself.

He picked up one day in a bookshop a book about the life and writings of a sixteenth-century Jewish Rabbi. Burgeon had never heard of the Rabbi before, and the whole subject was one about which he knew next to nothing. It just happened that his fancy was caught by the title: *Joseph Karo. Lawyer and Mystic.*

Karo had been a lawyer all right, in the Jewish sense of the term, and an extremely competent one. If you had the patience to find out as nearly as possible what 'halakha' meant, you could discover from the book, and confirm from your encyclopedia, that his powerful intellect had produced what was still the accepted textbook. Nor was he only an academic lawyer. He remained busy to the end of a long life, delivering opinions or judgments on practical matters like marriage and divorce, the devolution of property on death, and contractual and commercial relations. But all that was not the main subject of the biography. In addition to his great works, the *Bet Josef* and the *Shulhan Arukh*, Karo had left behind him a sort of private diary called *Maggid Mesharim*; and it was this book, and the problems connected with it, to which the author had devoted most of his attention.

It seemed that a Maggid was something like a voice that spoke within the mind 'in silence and solitude'. But not an audible voice. There were passages in the diary, confirmed by the witness of some of Karo's contemporaries, which indicated that when it did speak aloud it was with Karo's own voice. It

20

was not, however, peculiar to Karo. Visitation, or inspiration, by a Maggid was probably an accepted phenomenon in his time, though Karo appeared to be the outstanding example. Much of the book—after a learned textual and critical section which established the authenticity of the *Maggid Mesharim* in the face of early attempts to deny it—was concerned with 'Maggidism' in general. What exactly is, or was, a Maggid, in the view of a kabbalistic Rabbi of the sixteenth and seventeenth century and again in the light of twentieth-century psychology? These were questions on which no very clear conclusion was arrived at by the author, who had, however, been commendably lavish with his quotations. Among those quotations were the following:

'. . . we have seen demons or evil spirits entering men and troubling them . . . Similarly an angel may enter man and speak within him words of wisdom and this is what is generally called Maggid.'

'. . . and when thou awakest after having fallen asleep amid thoughts of the *Mishnah*, then it will speak in thy mouth and thy lips will vibrate . . . I am the *Mishnah* that speaketh in thy mouth . . .'

'The Shekhinah speaketh to you . . .'

And among the comments:

'The exact heavenly status of the Maggid is a matter of some ambiguity. As the *Mishnah* he/she may be considered to be identical with the divine *Logos* . . .'

'. . . the inducing of unreflected intuitions . . .'

'a peculiar technique of spontaneously producing discursive, intellectual, even highly specialized theoretical and speculative material without any conscious effort of thought.'

Burgeon never made a study of Karo or of Maggidism, but for a time after he had finished the book his mind, like *Hamlet*, was full of quotations. The part in which he was least interested was the commentary, exemplified in the last two of the quotations we have selected. Not because he despised it, but simply because he had read so much of the same sort in so many places. Symbolic clusters, the Unconscious, a psyche dominated by the mother-image, the 'active imagination' of Jung, yes, and even the Coleridgean 'repetition in the finite mind of the infinite I AM'—he was sick of them all. They were the everlasting professional device for substituting a plethora of *talk* about what mattered for—what actually mattered!

Two things stuck in his memory: one of them was that curious conception of the Maggid as the voice of the personified *Mishnah* (a voluminous record of written teachings) itself speaking. It was interesting to observe how, in the Hebrew mind, the two ideas of the 'Word', as the creative *Logos*, and the Word, as the inspired scriptural record, seemed to coalesce quite easily. The other was the fact that the Maggid had apparently been willing to answer questions concerning its own provenance.

It is a far cry from the Maggid to Lady Chatterley. Burgeon had nearly forgotten his own little experience and a considerable time elapsed before he became aware of any parallel between that half-abandoned question 'What should he make of it?' and the author's problem concerning the nature of the Maggid and Maggidism. In the end, however, it was just this parallel that made him turn to his own problem again. It had become more palpable, easier to think about. And for the first time the possibility occurred to him of deliberately seeking to repeat the experience and following where it led.

This was not a decision arrived at easily. If the inner depths of his being had detached themselves strangely that morning and become disturbingly expressive, its outer surface now threatened to do the same. Not for the first time in his life he encountered, almost as a separate and rather hostile entity, this matter-of-fact *persona* that bore his name and conducted the affairs of practical life—particularly his professional life—without much reference to him. On that previous occasion, years ago, when he had been in much greater difficulties, he had met the situation by acknowledging and even exaggerating the split personality that was distressing him. By doing so—and by writing a book about it—he had detached himself, just in time, from the *persona*, which he seemed to be in danger of actually becoming.

The acknowledgment had consisted in his bestowing on the *persona* a name like enough to, yet different enough from, his own—christening him 'Burden', in fact. So now, if we are to present adequately the sort of difficulties and obstacles which preceded Burgeon's decision on this occasion, we shall have to present them, as he himself did in those days, in the form of a dialogue between himself and this 'Burden'. At the same time, in case the reader may have begun to apprehend an irritating, para-Jamesian or neo-Proustian complexity of fragmented personality—with the fragments themselves personified for good measure, and Burgeon's psyche sprouting into a whole galaxy of invisible companions—we hasten to add that this is the one and only occasion on which Burden will appear.

Stripped of the inevitable interruptions and tedious repetitions which an interior colloquy of this sort necessarily involves, the dispute went something like this:

BURDEN: What is all the excitement about? You know perfectly well it is simply the old Neo-platonism turning up again. It's *always* turning up in one place or another. In different disguises.

BURGEON: Yes, but *why* is it always turning up? Suppose there has also always been good reason for it!

BURDEN: Oh, there's a reason all right. But my question just now is, why on earth should you be so interested in this *particular* disguise—the Kabbalistic one?

BURGEON: Why shouldn't I be, if I choose?

BURDEN: Incidentally, I thought you called yourself a Christian! I should have expected the Jewish context in which the whole thing is set to put you off—instead of drawing you on, as it seems to be doing.

BURGEON: That, I admit, is odd. The unfamiliar dress does rather attract me. But why shouldn't it? An unfamiliar dress may help you to see someone you have long known as if you were seeing him now for the first time. And that may be very important. Besides, doesn't it go to confirm what I was saying just now? If a people with such different roots back in the remote past, if even a people with a fundamentally *hostile* attitude to all gentile philosophy and gentile religion, can't help testifying—

BURDEN: Oh, all right, all right! But, whatever form it takes, pagan or Jewish or Christian, you know perfectly well there is a simple psychological explanation—

BURGEON: Simple?

BURDEN: No. It couldn't be simple. You've scored a point. But why pretend there's no such thing as the ordinary biology—and anthropology and psychology? Why treat it as anything more than the complicated subjective meanderings of the brain, which it obviously is?

BURGEON: When you say 'biology', you mean evolutionary biology, I suppose?

BURDEN: Certainly. We know how long it took the human brain to evolve, and we know something now of the emotional stresses, both adult and infantile, with which it has to cope. No wonder—

BURGEON: Coming down to brass tacks, you mean that evolution explains the Maggid?

BURDEN: Well, obviously!

BURGEON: But suppose the Maggid claims to explain evolution?

BURDEN: Did he? I didn't think evolution had been heard of in the sixteenth century.

BURGEON: No. I was thinking of my own experience.

BURDEN: Oho! We are already calling our affable familiar ghost that nightly—or at any rate *one* nightly—gulled us with intelligence 'the Maggid', are we! Burgeon! Chuck it! What on earth do you mean by it?

BURGEON: Leave that out for the moment, then. The point is that you explain both the Maggid and my own little experience in terms of a pre-existing world. Suppose they claim to explain the physical world in terms of their own pre-existence? How do I decide which to accept?

BURDEN: By using your common sense, man! I know you are confused by the part of your precious book that said the Maggid answered questions about his own nature. But surely every twopenny 'control' does the same for his medium! Subjective fantasy doesn't become less subjective by spreading itself on the topic of the objective world.

BURGEON: I don't really see how introducing the word 'subjective' helps us. It is simply a convenient way of begging the question. *Who* said *interior is anterior*? And how do I know it isn't right?

BURDEN: No one said it. It was a private reverie of your own.

BURGEON: No. No one *said* it. But . . . incidentally, don't the Oxford philosophers say there is no such thing as private reverie?

BURDEN: No. Not in that crude way. The difference between objective and subjective is the difference between the verifiable and the unverifiable.

BURGEON: So that if I say 'interior is anterior', that is unverifiable, but if I say 'interior is posterior', that can be easily verified?

BURDEN: Words, words, words! I doubt if either proposition really means anything at all.

24

BURGEON: Oh yes, they do. And you know perfectly well what they mean. The question is whether the immaterial—which we know as consciousness—came first in time and gave birth to the material—as has always been taken for granted by Oriental philosophy—or whether it is the other way round and the material world came first and gave birth to consciousness as a kind of epiphenomenon—as has recently been taken for granted by most Western thought. Meaning by 'recently' roughly since Darwin. Modern Science, in fact. It's a perfectly straightforward issue.

BURDEN: All verifiable facts are consistent with the latter hypothesis.

BURGEON: But are they *in*consistent with the former?

BURDEN: Yes. Because when you get to using words like 'immaterial' and 'consciousness', you are by definition outside the sphere of verification.

BURGEON: Whose definition? I don't want to be rude, but you see, my difficulty is that I don't understand what 'verification' can mean if it *doesn't* mean reference to the touchstone of immediate experience.

BURDEN: Well?

BURGEON: And I can't conceive of *any* more immediate experience than the one I had the other morning. Possibly it was the same with Karo.

BURDEN: You know very well that verification doesn't mean reference to *that* kind of experience.

BURGEON: What kind, then?

BURDEN: Normal experience.

BURGEON: How do you know it won't be normal one day—or even that it isn't becoming so already—in the less vociferous pockets of the community?

BURDEN: You're just wriggling. Normal experience of physical objects.

BURGEON: Oh, sweet 'verification'! It's all right when *you* do it, and all wrong when the other fellow takes your advice and gets a different result.

BURDEN: You choose to use the word in that impermissible way. But how do you propose to rule out the possibility that it was all memory—things you had once read and since forgotten?

BURGEON: How do I distinguish between an idea about the past and a memory of the past? Do I have to hunt up old diaries,

25

for instance? Of course not. I know a memory is a memory, because memories present themselves as such—immediately. They have a note of their origin endorsed on them. Well, the experience we are discussing was distinguishable from memory in the same intrinsic way that a memory is distinguishable from a fancy or an idea. I really don't see how any more ultimate verification is possible.

BURDEN: I say you didn't 'experience', as you call it, anything whatsoever.

BURGEON (*reflectively*): No. That really won't do, I'm afraid. In fact, it's absolute nonsense. You might as well tell me I don't exist!

BURDEN: But of *course* you don't!

BURGEON: Well, but, dash it, here I am talking to you! It's no use, Burden. You've done your best, but you beg all the questions. And, by the way, the most phoney thing about you is that insufferable, dead-pan cocksureness of yours. When we had that dust-up twenty years ago, it's true I pointed out—rightly— that it was *I* who originally brought *you* into being. But I was never so silly as to suggest that you didn't even exist.

BURDEN: By the way, what is all this leading up to?

BURGEON: Simply this. I propose to go on listening to what I hear—or to what I *overhear* thinking itself in my mind. If, of course, there is any more to hear. And if it seems worth while, perhaps—I don't know—perhaps I may some day record some of it.

BURDEN: You're on the slippery slope, governor!

BURGEON: Listen. You know what the expression *Without Prejudice* means? You ought to, if anyone does . . . lawyer!

BURDEN: Nonsense! Nonsense!

BURGEON: Remember what Herbert Spencer said? A man after your own heart, if ever there was one!

BURDEN: Nonsense! What's that got to do with it? What did he say?

BURGEON: 'There is a principle which is proof against all argument and which cannot fail to keep a man in everlasting ignorance: that principle is contempt prior to investigation.' Further investigation without prejudice. That will be my attitude Whether it's worth anything; whether there is any wisdom in it, are matters I can judge on their own merits—just as I can judge anything else.

BURDEN: You keep on talking about 'it'. I wish you—

BURGEON: And what's more, I shall call it the Maggid.

BURDEN: Surely, that's plain silly. You say you're going to 'record' something. I suppose that means that you are going to write about it. Or rather that *I* am, since I'm your behaviour. We shall get off on the wrong foot straight away. They'll take it as *pastiche*.

BURGEON: There's something in that. On the other hand— my difficulty is this. To help keep me 'without prejudice', I need a word with no other associations whatsoever; a word that simply means 'the source of information—if it is information— obtained in that sort of way' and means nothing else. I dislike *inventing* names—there is something brash about it. Now, it happens, in fact, to have been the Karo book that put into my head the idea of giving it a name at all—and Werblowsky— that's the author—does use the word *Maggid* very largely without prejudice. I have the advantage—from this point of view—of *not* knowing Hebrew. On the whole I believe it's a good thing to keep the connection.

BURDEN: Please yourself—but don't say you haven't been warned. You know what readers are. Nothing will stop them from saying you have drawn, not just this word, but the whole substance of your book, from the literature of Jewish mysticism. It will probably be called a cunning re-hash of the Kabbalah.

BURGEON: But I don't know anything about the Kabbalah!

BURDEN: That won't worry them, old fellow. Nor will they!

BURGEON: What about varying it slightly and calling it the *Meggid*?

BURDEN: Oh, call it what you like. But what are you proposing to *do*?

BURGEON: I shall wait in all humility to see if some time it— no, if *he*, will go on where he left off. Karo's Maggid sometimes used to, after quite a long interval. And I shall hope to learn from him some day something about his own nature.

After this initial flare-up, the Burden element in Burgeon gave no more trouble; at least, it gave no more on *this* issue. It knew when it was beaten and it had decided to accept the inevitable. The way is now clear therefore, for the record that follows of some of Burgeon's own further encounters with 'the Meggid'.

THREE

About a week elapsed before the surrounding circumstances were favourable for a further approach. And then the first question that arose was the right way to make it. Cautiously Burgeon began by recalling the former occasion. He had started then by reflecting on a conversation he had had with two friends about the Lady Chatterley trial and about D. H. Lawrence and his followers in general. Should he simply repeat? At first he rejected the idea; he had no wish to identify the light which the Meggid seemed willing to shed on the dark places in his mind with this particular dark place—the enigma of Lawrence's reputation as a prophet. He did not feel it to be important enough. But then he also remembered that this first encounter had been left unfinished. The information he had received had revealed itself by its very nature as a mere introduction, a beginning. Perhaps . . .

He dragged his mind back once more to that inconclusive conversation with Rodney and Middleton or what he could still recall of it, back to a point that had been touched on and then, like so much else, left hanging in the air. Someone had said— someone called Burgeon (but that was now irrelevant) had pointed to essentials in the evolution of the Western world that Lawrence had been obliged to 'write off' in order to make his doctrine hold water. And now he placed side by side with that recollection one of the passages from *Lady Chatterley's Lover*, which Counsel for the Prosecution had read to the Jury in his closing speech. It recalled Lady Chatterley's reflections in the act of copulation.

'What liars the poets and everybody were! They made one think one wanted sentiment. When what one supremely wanted was this piercing, consuming, rather awful sensuality . . .'
And again:
'The supreme pleasure of the mind! And what is that to a

woman? What is it, really, to the man either! He becomes merely messy and doggy, even in his mind. It needs sheer sensuality even to purify and quieten the mind . . .'

Burgeon decided to let his own mind dwell a little on some of those 'written off' phenomena in the history of Western man. He recalled the closing lines of a sonnet from the *Vita Nuova*:

> *Quel ch'ella par quand'un poco sorride,*
> *Non si puo dicer, ne tener a mente,*
> *Si è nuovo miracolo gentile.*

Would that, for Lawrence, be included under the heading of 'merely messy and doggy'? Presumably so. Burgeon resisted a strong temptation to feel that he had scored a point—to anything resembling an inward sneer. He simply set the question before him and contemplated it. 'The poets and *nearly everybody* —' But then, it was not Lawrence speaking in his own person, it was a character in one of his novels—and at a highly charged moment. Still, it was as a prophet that they presented Lawrence, not primarily as a novelist. 'Sex in the head.' It seemed to follow from the whole nexus that that must cover—well, for instance, the whole of the *Divine Comedy*. The whole? Most of the second half, anyway. Botticelli's and Raphael's Madonnas . . . the Cathedrals . . . St. Bernard . . . The Rose of Paradise . . . The *Romance of the Rose* . . . 'Sex in the heart' . . . Burgeon felt that the Meggid had begun to speak. And it told him in no uncertain terms to go back before going on, and to look first at the source, which it now disclosed to him. He saw quite clearly that mysterious potency on its way down from the head to the lower organism. He saw it reach the heart and the blood and from there begin to manifest itself in a new way, a way of which the Greek world had as yet had no experience— and of which Lawrence and most of the twentieth century *no longer* had any experience. He saw it radiating outward from within, as it had once rayed formatively inward from without— then, when it was hardly yet aware of itself as physical. He saw the beginnings of that awareness taking shape already in the Middle Ages; and then the Meggid left him for a while to continue with his own reflections.

The *Romance of the Rose* of Guillaume de Lorris, he thought— but also of Jean de Meun! He recalled the figure of Genius, the priest of Venus, in that complex and rambling medieval allegory, the priest of 'potency'. A strange irruption into the ritual of 'Courtly Love'! Courtly love? Courtesy itself as an ingredient in human behaviour looked like becoming outmoded. And yet how much of past and expended Europe it contained! *Eros* and *Agape* . . . the rise, florescence and decline of Chivalry . . . love itself—except so far as it was identified with that exclusively erotic 'tenderness' to which Lawrence and the witnesses for the Defence had paid so much attention . . . But Burgeon realized that he was going too fast. He had better keep his mind upon what he knew of medieval allegory and courtly love. It was not nearly as much as he could have wished. Nevertheless his business now was to contemplate what he did know.

Clearly the first thing to do was to recall the opening chapters of Lewis's *Allegory of Love*. It had all begun with Ovid; and Ovid was much nearer to the Greeks than to the Middle Ages. Had the Meggid been telling him, then, that sex, even in Ovid's *Art of Love*, was 'not yet aware of itself as physical'? That was about as absurd a statement as a man could make. And yet—the Meggid must surely be right; and he began to divine that it would be just when the Meggid said the most seemingly outrageous things that it would be telling him most—if he knew how to resolve the enigma. This one resolved itself quickly. Of course Ovid knew, of course everyone knew at all times, the physical component. Yet that was not the same as sex being aware of itself as physical. Ovid had not taken sex seriously. It was precisely because he concentrated on the physical (and Burgeon recalled his own definition of 'lust') that Ovid could not take sex seriously. Try to convince Ovid that the sexual act was the manifestation of a potency with metaphysical implications and a significance far beyond itself, and he would have laughed in your face. *He* would have been the first to agree that the witness for the Defence were 'solemn asses'. His own solemnity had been a very different matter. It had been put on for fun. It had been, in Lewis's memorable phrase, 'funny as the ritual solemnity of old gentlemen over their wine is funny'.

Lewis had pointed out how the medieval allegory of love had formed itself by taking this solemnity literally and converting it into a *real* solemnity. And now the Meggid had told him why that unlikely development had occurred. The potency, which made the sexual act possible and could be recognized in it—but which also made so much else possible—had found its way down from the head to the heart. There it had indeed awakened to a new awareness of itself—and, of course, what it became aware of was not the potency of physical sex, for physical sex is not in the heart but in the loins; it was the potency of feeling, of feeling in all its subtlest and gentlest overtones.

Sex in the heart—and what next? Where did we go from there? Lawrence was right, then? The potency, or rather its awakening to awareness of itself, must have sunk down lower still—into the loins. That was where it had last been awakening. For a moment he recalled the cant use of that very word in a typical publisher's blurb: 'This novel portrays with disconcerting candour the awakening of a sheltered adolescent, etc. etc.' There is one respect, he decided, in which even cant may be genuine—it may be genuinely a symptom. And Lawrence had had the penetration to see below the symptom. Twentieth-century man was dimly, gropingly, feebly finding the potency where it actually was—within; within the physical frame where a man was separate and alone. But Lawrence had also divined the truth that, although it was within him, it did not belong to him. It was his surviving real link with the cosmos, out of which even his separateness had been born. It was his present being.

But Burgeon was on his guard against empty speculation, however lofty—then most, indeed, when it began to be 'lofty'. He suddenly turned round from it and asked the Meggid point-blank what connection there was between this last train of thought—should he call it 'the descent of the potency'?—and the other piece of information which he had received on the first occasion, concerning the delicate structure, formed from within, in the brain, and at the same time in the reproductive organs. And what was the purpose of that structure? The answer to the second question came first and came instantly; it was 'for fertilization'. The answer to the second was slow and hesitant. It was as if the Meggid wanted to throw him a line, but was anxious lest he should become entangled with it; as if it wanted to hurry him over it, in case he should become too pedantically involved. First, it reminded him of an expression which Karo's Maggid had himself used, and used more than once, concerning the Shekhinah. The Shekhinah was in *exile*; it was forlorn and poverty-stricken. And it could be redeemed from its poverty only by the spiritual exertions of the devout, who could 'participate' in the exile of the Shekhinah. It reminded him, too, that

31

Karo's Maggid, though at other times he spoke directly, had more than once spoken of himself as identical with the Shekhinah. 'Sweeter than honey the gift of the Queen to them that wander with her in exile!'

What was it—what was it that Lawrence himself always spoke of as feeble and poverty-stricken, something which for Burgeon himself had such different associations? His memory recalled it. It was the 'logos'. The logos, to Lawrence, meant the insipidity of intellect, because intellect had no potency.

'There is nothing of me that is alone and absolute except my mind, and we shall find that the mind has no existence by itself, it is only the glitter of the sun on the surface of the waters.'

Only!

'. . . so that my individualism is really an illusion. I am part of the great whole and I can never escape. But I *can* deny my connections, break them, and become a fragment. Then I am wretched.

Do I exist?

But *of course* you don't! Burden had said.

At last it was clear. The potency had become his own in order that he, having become himself, might give it back to the logos, whence it had descended, leaving behind it an impotent shell. Either it must be given back *or* . . . and he saw them so clearly now in his mind's eye, the forces that had gone into the development of that delicate structure and were now set free. There were two opposite directions in which they could move; he saw them, like a crowd of boys set free from school, rushing off madly in the wrong direction; down, down, down into the loins, to find, in extinction, release from the intolerable divine energy which they were.

He was excited and tired and they suddenly began clamouring, those forces, to go the same sweet way in his own body. Into the tuck-shop . . . No!

There was little more free time left. He said good-bye for the time being to the Meggid and strove to sum up for the last time what he now knew about D. H. Lawrence and his followers. They were right, a thousand times, in their insistence that the everlasting 'sex' with which the twentieth century is obsessed to the verge of demonic possession is infinitely more than the surface thrill as which it was mostly accepted, infinitely more also than a basis of intimate companionship between persons of opposite sex; infinitely more than the means to the procreation of children. They were right in divining through it a mightiness that had been shackled and should now be set free. In all else, how desperately wrong! Things could not remain as they had been. What had been set free must flow either in one direction or the other.

'She came to the very heart of the jungle of herself. She felt, now, she had come to the real bedrock of her nature, and was essentially shameless. She was herself, naked and unashamed . . . She felt a triumph, almost a vainglory. So! That was how it was! That was life! That was how oneself really was!'

Either down into animalism or back into the 'logos'—of which Lawrence knew nothing, which Lawrence found insipid, as a man finds the music of Bach insipid who has only so far learned to compare hot jazz on the one hand with drawing-room ballads on the other.

They were not wrong about the insipidity, and the impotence, of the only kind of thinking they recognized; the kind that had brought about the industrial civilization in which they were all embedded from childhood and which had seared the sensitive soul of the child Lawrence instead of simply murdering it. But no; the tragedy was deeper than that. It was not that kind of thought that had brought about industrial civilization, just as it was not that kind that could ever bring any other to birth within its womb. The impotent kind was indeed the kind that industrial civilization itself brought about in its turn, once it was established. What remedy? What remedy? Sex in the head, sex in the heart, sex in the loins—and what next? Fertilization. The pity of it, Iago! The desperate cry, going up from a world more out of joint than ever before in its long history, for creative mind and for the treasury of knowledge which that alone can unlock from the strong-room whither it has been withdrawn, to set us free—and the solemn Messianic response, delivered in three million copies at 3s. 6d. each, that enthusiastic copulation is pretty well all that is required to set it right!

FOUR

'He was such a dear little chap,' said the Mother, 'even a year ago! And now there's nothing.'

Burgeon waited apprehensively. And sure enough:

'I wish you'd have a talk with him,' she said.

He was in the house of a Builder client, for whom he had acted for many years. Besides buyings and sellings of houses, there had been some family complications with collaterals, a deed of family arrangement, a will. During the war Burgeon had been able to put a cottage in his way, where he could evacuate his family. It had all been easy enough, but for some reason the Builder was lastingly grateful to him. He was a nice Builder, with a nice wife. Burgeon was regarded, with affection and respect, as a friend of the family; and he liked the feeling. But he didn't like it much just now.

The Builder had had to go out, and his wife, the mother of three, had insisted on giving her guest a sort of high tea before his departure. The two older children were out in the world; the youngest had just left school and was earning good money in some not very satisfactory blind-alley occupation. They had heard him, while they were doing their business, come in from work and switch on the 'telly' in the next room.

The Mother went to the door and opened it. 'Willy', she called out, 'come and say how d'you do to Mr. Burgeon before he goes.' The 'telly' continued, unabated. 'Oh, *come* on!' she called again, and after some further delay the imbecile pop song was stopped in its tracks and Willy appeared, complete with the tight trousers, tousled head and slight scowl which Burgeon's talk with the Mother had led him to expect.

'Hullo, Willy,' he said with a geniality in his voice which his heart had not sufficient energy to authenticate; but which seemed justified by the fact that he had seen the boy from time to time since he was a baby.

'I'll just take these things out and get them washed up,' said the Mother and disappeared through the door, closing it behind her.

'How's it going?'

'All right.'

'That's fine.'

After an awkward pause—or rather a pause which made Burgeon feel awkward, he added:

'Your mother seems a bit worried about you.'

'Why?' said Willy. 'I don't do her any harm.'

'Oh, one way and another,' said Burgeon lamely. 'Women do worry,' he added, trying desperately to make contact on a male trade-union ticket. 'She says you aren't interested in anything.'

'What is there to be interested in?'

Burgeon was nonplussed—also irritated. 'Well—' He hesitated. 'One hardly knows where to begin. I should have thought you'd be saying what *isn't* there to be interested in.'

'F'r instance?' said the youth remorselessly.

Burgeon felt himself perspiring slightly. It was a bad choice, and he knew it, but for some reason he couldn't think of anything else. 'Do you know the names of any of the stars, for example, and where to find them?'

'That sort of lark's O.K. for squares. They can have it.'

There was a long pause. Burgeon decided not to enumerate any further interesting topics.

'Got a girl-friend?'

'Girls!' said Willy enigmatically and Burgeon had not the faintest idea what, if anything, was going on in the boy's mind. Another pause.

'Belong to a youth club?'

'All wet. Run by old squares for young squares.'

Burgeon looked cravenly at his watch and got up. The Mother returned.

'You're not going, Mr. Burgeon?' And to Willy: 'I hoped you'd be in the middle of telling Mr. Burgeon some of the things you never tell me.'

Her son assumed a slightly American accent, as he replied:

'Doyng! Cut the crap, Mom, please!'

'We haven't got very far,' said Burgeon. 'Perhaps some other time—' And out in the passage, as she opened the door for him, he told her (without conviction) that he expected it was a passing phase and her beloved son would soon be pulling himself together and taking hold of life.

Next day, by a coincidence, Burgeon was visited at his office by a client called James, a young man of about thirty, who wanted to arrange a surrender of his tenancy of a disused workshop in South London. He had been using it for a few months as a café (carefully avoiding the word 'club') for teenagers and he had just decided, with great reluctance, that he must give it up. His financial resources were not great and he felt he could not face the rapid depreciation of furniture and equipment and even of the premises themselves (for which he was, of course, responsible to the landlord) which the project involved. He outlined the situation and Burgeon, after promising to write to the landlord's solicitors, began asking him a few questions.

'I suppose,' he said, 'replacements of crockery alone must be quite a heavy expense?'

'Oh no. We don't use crockery. The cups and saucers and plates are all unbreakable. They would have to be.'

'For throwing about, you mean?'

'Yes. It's not that. They're plastic and don't really hurt when they hit you. It's more the furniture.'

'But surely they don't throw *that* about?'

'Not so much throwing about—of course, I get an occasional chair thrown at me, but mostly it's just smashing. Not all the time, of course. You get a sudden wave of it and the whole place becomes an inferno for a bit. Then it calms down again.'

'Do these young people not understand that the furniture has been provided solely for their own benefit? Isn't it possible to explain that to them? What do they imagine you have been doing it all for?'

'Yes. You can try. Some of them seem to take it in. But underneath they don't believe it. They think it's all part of the Establishment—though they're not sophisticated enough to use words like that—and that the Establishment's getting at them— and anyway will look after itself, whatever they do.'

'Hm,' said Burgeon, remembering Willy. 'What on earth's really at the back of it? Children didn't use to behave like that, not even the tough ones.'

'Hardly children,' said James. And then, resignedly: 'We can't find out what it is. That's part of the trouble.'

'I suppose there's no doubt they have too much money to spend.'

'Yes,' said James, 'that's one thing. Too much flattering publicity is another. It's a pity the word "teenager" was ever invented.'

'Why?'

'Oh, I don't know. Every silly thing they do is *news*. It's solemnly discussed—'

'—in the way we're discussing it now—'

'I suppose so. The stage and the Press cash in on it. Pop singers are given interviews—asked their opinions on marriage or religion or the Common Market or what have you. Teenagers are encouraged to regard themselves as a kind of institution.'

'—instead of just getting spanked!' put in Burgeon reflectively.

James hardly heard him. 'It must go much deeper than all that,' he said thoughtfully. 'Of course, they don't go to plays—at least mine don't—but the plays are a true reflection. They've got it in their blood somehow, this business that anything with a root in the past is contemptible.'

'There's the bomb, of course. In my time the Establishment did at least look firmly established.'

'Yes. I do think there is an element of unconscious fear. But it's not the main thing.'

'Perhaps they feel that, whether it blows up or not, *this* Establishment isn't really established *on* anything—that it doesn't really believe in itself.'

James had a slightly annoying habit of not being nearly as impressed by Burgeon's contributions to the discourse as you would have expected him to be. He seemed to be struggling on with the problem in his mind.

'What is it?' he said. 'There is this impassable barrier between one of them and—and *any* adult, however friendly, however tough, however little nonsense there is about him—just because he *is* an adult.'

'An "oldster", in fact?'

'Yes. It is taken for granted that he can't even be listened to. Everything he may say has been judged worthless in advance. How do we make contact?'

'It seems to me that the answer is we don't. It doesn't sound much fun to me.'

'Do you know,' said James, 'the torturing thing is to see all that *energy*—human energy, after all—even in their destructiveness—to see it systematically murdering itself.'

'Where does it come from, eh?' said Burgeon.

James did not answer and Burgeon found himself thinking that that was a question he might one day put to the Meggid.

'Well,' he said aloud, 'I think you'll be well out of it. What are you going to do instead?'

'I shall find somewhere else, I suppose.'

'But the same thing will happen!'

'*I* don't know,' said James with sudden irritation. 'I shall have to find some other way, then.'

'What do you mean, you'll have to? Who's making you?'

'We just can't leave all those young things to destroy themselves. Through no fault of their own.'

'I'm not so sure about that.'

'If it is their fault, they don't know it is—and have no means of knowing. They'll *never* know that or anything else, unless we do something. But what?'

Burgeon felt humiliated, or rather humbled, which is not quite the same thing. 'Didn't someone once say,' he remarked, '*In order that evil may triumph, all that is necessary is for good men to do nothing?*'

James looked at him, more appreciatively than he had yet done, and smiled.

'Anyway,' he said, 'get me out of that lease, will you!'

He shook hands with Burgeon and left.

But the Meggid, when Burgeon was next able to hear him, did not seem particularly interested in the ways and problems of teenagers. Burgeon had prepared himself by thinking back to the last encounter and reviewing both the information he had then received and the conclusions he had afterwards reached; and with this in his mind he had sought for more light on the problem that was troubling James and the Builder's wife, and a good many other people, including now himself.

The Meggid's response was nearly as unexpected as his original utterance had been.

You know now' he seemed to begin by saying, that interior is anterior; that is to say, you must look to the interior for the origin. But that is not enough. Because I told you of 'forces' entering into and developing the brain you are now thinking of the interior realm as a field of force, and because the question we were then concerned with was 'potency', you are thinking of it, as so many psychoanalysts do, as a sort of formless reservoir of potency, which is only differentiated in the moment of its physical manifestation. But that is not the case.

You mean, said Burgeon (for these encounters can only be expressed in the form of conversation), that there are different kinds of forces?

I mean that there are different beings. Forces are only the end-product of their activity. If you are to be any use at need, you must learn to distinguish the beings themselves.

Surely, said Burgeon, I should first need to have access to this 'realm' you speak of. Do you really suggest I am fit for it?

No. You are not fit for it. But, because time presses, you *have* access. Indeed, you are there already. Otherwise you would not be hearing me. For it is there that I am.

I will listen—without prejudice.

That is a good answer. If you listened in any other way, it would not be my voice you would hear, but some other's. I am telling you now of two such beings. It is their office, among other things, to shape the subtler part of the biological evolution, and to gather and guide the unconscious drives of humanity. There are others with the same task, but with those you need not now concern yourself. What you must know is that they take the lead in turn. The first of the two I am speaking of was effective for a few hundred years until towards the end of the last century. Then the second took over from him.

I must try to characterize them to you by the very different manners of their working. I will use the word 'logos' because it is familiar to you, and you have had to consider it recently in connection with Lawrence's peculiar use of it. You know—

I know almost nothing.

You are prepared, then, to think without prejudice that the logos is present in two distinguishable ways, on the one hand in the outer world and on the other hand in the mind. Lawrence wrote as if he had only heard of the second way, but, because the body is part of the outer world, the logos is present both in the body and in the mind of man. Both these beings are servants of the logos. They are named—

The Meggid hesitated. You could not have said—as Karo

39

sometimes did—that he actually 'stammered'; but there was a definite hesitation, and for a moment Burgeon had the impression of an almost sorrowful reluctance, as of one about to trample perforce on holy ground.

They are called—others have had other names for them—names are of no importance—yet it was of great use to you to find a name for *me*?—I do not say it is the best name you could have found, but I am content with it. In that case it was best you should find your own—but not in this. They may be named—as Karo's Maggid, too, would have named them—Gabriel and Michael.

It is no accident that Gabriel has always been recognized by Christians as the angel of the Annunciation; for incarnation, the becoming flesh of spirit, is the core of his impulse and activity. For the ordinary run of mankind he is effective in all that they develop through the operation of physical heredity.

Darwin! exclaimed Burgeon.

Do not interrupt. Listen. During the three or four centuries of Gabriel's hegemony the forces of heredity worked very strongly through the whole of Western civilization. You need not for the present trouble yourself with the East. Men experienced his working as the warmth with which they felt all that linked them together in this way—with their ancestors, with their children and their children's children, and with each other, in so far as the others were of the same blood. You have heard me say this. When you go away, test it from all you know without my help—from your acquaintance, for example, such as it is, with the history, and perhaps especially the literature, of England and the rest of Europe during the period I am speaking of. But do not go away yet.

There are other quite different ways in which this being's activity impels, and one of them is this. Dwell on the full meaning of the word *incarnation*. It does not refer only to human flesh, or even only to flesh. It refers to the whole world of nature, in so far as that is perceived through the senses; and it was to this world of the senses that Gabriel directed the earnest gaze of mankind. It is this world that they have been minding more and more through the last three or four hundred years—so assiduously, at last, that they have begun to believe there is no other. And even that there has never been any other.

Had they not done so, they could never have built up their

technological civilization, with its evil and its good. You may now, if you like, think of Darwin and his co-workers and successors. Here the Gabrielic impulsion was doubly strong; for there was not only the growing warmth of enthusiasm for a purely physical science; *that* applied to *all* the sciences. But here the enthusiasm was truly at home, for the field of its operation was also the field of heredity itself. You—who know *something* at least of other equally important factors in the evolution of humanity—have you any better explanation for the unbalanced obsession with biology which has held the idea of evolution in its grip ever since it first began to be entertained in the West?

And now, my friend, recall what you learned from me before of the structure in the front part of the brain. Interior is anterior, and this, too, was an incarnation, as long as the structure was in process of formation. It is otherwise now that the forces which informed it have finished their work and been set free.

Like the Spirit in *Comus*, said Burgeon:

> *Now my task is smoothly done*
> *I can fly or I can run* . . .

I shall leave you now, said the Meggid.

Burgeon was left alone. Once again, as he rose and bent himself to the tasks of the day, the whole context receded to a remote distance; yet it was not quite so remote as before. Instead of dismissing it from his mind, in the course of the next few days he followed the Meggid's advice and endeavoured to test the unaccountable data. Heredity. Pedigree. Dynasty. He recalled the enormous part played by the will-to-dynasty in the history of Europe, as the picture of the Holy Roman Empire faded increasingly from men's minds; the persistence of the concept of dynasty as a survival until, say, 1914 and its almost headlong disappearance thereafter. He thought of the biographies he knew and of the contrast between the old nineteenth-century style and the modern. They spread themselves in those days! You began with an account of the family going back at least three generations, and often more. And it wasn't only biographies. Even the *novelists* of the eighteenth and nineteenth centuries often began in much the same way before the hero came on the stage in his cradle. But who thought of doing that today?

Then there was the heavily dynastic approach to marriage

prevalent throughout the older European drama, and still forming, together with the romantic revolt against it, the background of these same nineteenth-century novels. And not only novels either. It still shone out sharply, it still even operated faintly, in the typical marriage settlement that formed the root of so many of the titles to land he had had to investigate in the early years of his practice. Heredity and hereditary status, not as a theory—heredity as a positive, warm experience—was at the root of the whole law of real property. Was that why articled clerks used to find it so difficult to understand? Heirlooms and entail—'the first and each succeeding son of her body'. What a different world it must have been! But you didn't need to go as far as entail. Even 'fee simple' had tacitly included unborn heirs in the concept—no, in the present *fact*—of ownership; until the puzzling old 'Rule in Shelley's Case' was abolished as an anachronism in 1925.

Of course, there were also some negative reactions, but overall the result of the test was positive enough to make him very sure of one thing; and that was that he wished to hear more. Therefore, when the next favourable opportunity arose he waited in hopes that the Meggid would continue where he had left off. Nor was he disappointed. This time the Meggid began by gently insisting that it was really not at all difficult to see that 'interior' forces, which have been producing a physical form by incarnating, are set free when their work is completed. It happens, he said, over much of the earth every autumn. When the stem and leaves, and at last the flower, have been given physical form, we glimpse their departure in the revelation of light and colour and scent which ascend from the blossom like a cloud, on their way back to immateriality. When you have learnt to see this happening with eyes that can see a little, and it is only a very little, beyond the physical, you will see also the difference between the only way of thinking that was open to the Gabriel age —and the way which is open to the age that is now upon us. The disengagement of the interior forces has enabled a thinking without any hereditary, any sanguine, any physical support. Such thinking, added the Meggid—and Burgeon could conceive something like a twinkle in his eye—if it also refrains from leaning on tradition or authority—is indeed, and for the first time, 'without prejudice'.

But Burgeon was far from satisfied that he understood. I

remember, he said, that you spoke before of another being, who bears the same relation to this age that Gabriel did to the age that is just past. How then is the difference so great? You named him—

Wait, said the Meggid. You are in too much haste. You have heard what I had to say, and you have sought to test it. I do not ask if you are satisfied with the test, for that is a matter only for you. But before you try to think any farther, have you really comprehended *how* the thinking of that former age was 'physical'?

Burgeon recalled some of the negative reactions to his test. No, he said, to be honest, I do not feel that I have. There are difficulties. The very word 'physical' . . . Against a period that ended before the close of the nineteenth century you have set this present period. It would seem to follow that the thinking of this present period is less 'physical'. Yet, when I look about me, it seems, in fact, to be *more* physical, more exclusively physical than it has ever been. It may be that in certain departments of science it is not so—but I am not sure even about that. It is certainly so in philosophy, in the academic philosophy that has become predominant even during my own lifetime; and outside that there is the huge devastated area of Marxism!

The Meggid took him up quickly: You must learn to distinguish. The Western world is indeed full of thoughts *about* the physical. But that is not what I meant by physical thinking. The thinking you now have in mind is not physically and sensuously informed. It is brain-physical only. There is a thinking determined by the brain alone; and there is, or was, a thinking warmed, as it were, and founded as well in the whole physique other than the brain.

If it is determined by the brain, is it not 'physical'?

Yes, indeed. I said, of the kind of thinking to which I am seeking to draw your attention, that it is 'open to' mankind today. I did not say that the opening had been found. Yet even now, and before the opening has been found, this modern thinking is non-physical by comparison. And that is true even of Marxism.

Burgeon sought to digest this. This typical modern thinking which *I* have in mind, he asked—I will call it 'materialism'—is *that* 'without prejudice'?

Not very often. It is so in the special sense in which I used your own pet phrase just now, in an endeavour to help you. But it does not fulfil the other condition. It leans very heavily, though unconsciously, on authority; for those who practise it are unwilling even to consider any idea not sanctioned by the authority on which *they* rely. At its best, it *is* 'without prejudice' —but also without potency. It is impotent. Is not that what you are all discovering? Is not that what Lawrence discovered? And is not that very discovery the root of the trouble with the young people you asked me about?

Perhaps. But before we return to that—I am still not clear. You yourself reminded me that the sense of potency is no longer in the brain—as it was, for instance, with the Greeks—but has descended from there. How, then, could this new way of thinking that you say has been released be *other* than impotent?

I said that forces had been released. Forces that can create by incarnating—are they impotent? You must distinguish. Non-physical thinking about the physical is still of the brain. Non-physical thinking about the non-physical can become *wholly* non-physical. It can become those very forces.

I think, said Burgeon, greatly daring, it is perhaps you who are now hastening on too fast. I am not wholly with you.

Listen, said the Meggid earnestly. You were about to ask me just now how the being whom I named Michael exercises his hegemony. Try now to picture it. He does not work indirectly through the flesh or through the senses. His field is the thinking that has been set free from the flesh. He is in the light, but not the physical light. He seeks to descend on the wings of that light into the nest which Gabriel has built for him in the minds of individual men.

But Burgeon remained stubborn. This thinking 'about the non-physical', he said, is very dubious. All words—ideas—have their memory-traces of sensation. Can you offer me an example?

Have you not found *me*? said the Meggid, and he added, after a long pause: I am one of the least of Michael's servants.

It was several weeks later before Burgeon was again in touch with the Meggid. It was not only that he needed, as before, to test what he had heard against his previous experience and judgment. He felt a little afraid. Anything in the nature of numinous awe seemed out of place in his whole relation with the Meggid, and yet—what manner of responsibility was he assuming? This time, when the encounter came, it came of its own accord. He was thinking—and the Meggid spoke. He was thinking, but without any intention of approach, about the Meggid's reference to light. All that he had said about the Michael age had somehow culminated in that unusually poetic remark about a descent 'on the wings of light'. Yet light was something outside you in space. How was he to reconcile that with all that had previously been said, and indeed emphasized, about interiority? Interiority, by the way, was an ugly word, but he could not think of a better. Anyway, the point was that everything the Meggid had previously said appeared to be founded on it. It was in that direction, after all, that he had, in fact, *found* the Meggid!

It was at this point in his reflection that the Meggid spoke.

You are using the term 'interior' to yourself, he said, as if it meant deeper and deeper inside your body. In fact, it means almost the opposite. When I said 'interior is anterior', I was not using it in that way. I can best put it by saying that I meant by 'interior' nearer to where you eventually found *me*. You ought to know better than to think that this 'interior' is so situated that it can be reached by more and more infinitesimal dissection. You ought to know better than to even *half*-imagine that by penetrating the brain you will read the thought.

I really think I do know better than that, said Burgeon meekly.

Well, but you keep forgetting. The brain is related to thinking as the eye is to light. But it is the paradox, it is the mystery, of the Michael age that you can test the objectivity of thinking only by making it most deeply and intimately your own. And that, after all, is what you are doing with me. Before you reflect any further about the nature of light, there is something I would say to you. You are fond, you know, of having things in aphoristic form. If you are still disposed to make a sheet-anchor of 'interior is anterior'—add this to it, as a rider, that 'Space is both interior and exterior'.

I will do so, said Burgeon.

You have been wondering, began the Meggid again, from time to time during the last few weeks, how all this should have arisen from the question you brought to me about the forlorn state of those young people. I will try now to tell you.

But where shall I begin? Perhaps at some such point as this. You are aware that, in the development of the theory of evolution, a good deal has been written, sometimes with more, sometimes with less, conviction, about a certain striking relation between phylogenesis and ontogenesis—a relation of recapitulation or analogy, or both. I would have you know that this is only a faint and crude reflection of the reality; and that is because the evolution, which is supposed, takes no account of that process of incarnation, of which you and I have spoken much. The *real* process is indeed repeated and recapitulated at all levels and over all manner of periods of time. Wherever you look you will find that sequence: the descent of immaterial forces into the material, which they create by so descending, followed by their setting free and re-ascent. We have had before us a period of some three or four hundred years. We could also have taken a period as long as the whole history of the earth. And I gave you an example of a still briefer cycle, when I instanced the growth of a plant from seed to flower and back again to the seed.

But it is again the same in the life and growth of any individual human being. The individual—shall I say, 'potency'?—which descends into the embryo and begins its work of informing, finishes the different stages of its work at different times during his life and is then progressively set free.

You speak, said Burgeon, of an individual potency—choosing, I suppose, a term which you think familiar to me. I know it was much in my mind on the occasion when I first recognized you. Do you mean that the man existed *as* an individual before his birth, before his conception?

The Meggid remained silent; and Burgeon had the curious impression that his silence arose from embarrassment. Does your silence, he enquired at last—does your silence mean that the answer is so obvious that I ought never to have asked the question?

It does indeed, replied the Meggid. But let me continue, please. The earlier stages of release—I mean, of course, the release of the informing forces—are evinced by easily perceptible and outwardly physical signs. The latter are more subtle, but we are not concerned with them. The physical process of second dentition is the product of the first release. Before that stage in childhood is reached, mind and body are one in a way that the man will never know again.

Mind and body! We are talking of 'forces'.

Do not interrupt.—We have already agreed that there are two ways in which the logos is present in man.—It is the next stage, the second release, to which I wish you to give your attention. When he reaches the age of puberty, it is because the informing forces have completed a further stage of their work and are correspondingly released. The man experiences this, in part, as a new independence of mind. Before, he imitated; now he is ready to pass *judgment* on his environment. But he also experiences the potency direct—with a new intensity—and more nearly in its own nature, *as* potency—now that it is continuing to work only in part of his being instead of through the whole. Mind and body begin trying to go their separate ways. He is tormented in one way or another by the gulf between them.

This is very interesting, said Burgeon, but surely it is not something which only happens in our time? It must have been happening to adolescents for thousands of years past.

That is true. But between the age that is just past and the age in which the child of today experiences adolescence there is the great difference which I have shown you. Adult thinking itself— the adult thinking towards which adolescence is a reaching-out— had not yet been fully released from tutelage, as it is today.

Tutelage?

I have told you of a Gabriel age. But call it the tutelage of 'instinct', if you will. One who knows that interior is anterior knows also that the logos is present in instinct as well as in mind. In the past the growing child could accord an instinctive respect to grown-up minds which were held in the same nimbus of instinct as his own. His judgment could accept their judgments with a certain reverence. And that is what he needs above all things in the period *before* puberty. Already, in that period, he can no longer be satisfied with merely imitating his elders, as he did when he was still a baby. But he is not yet self-determined enough to meet their judgments with his own, as equal to equal. He needed, in those earlier years of his, not so much to 'think for himself'—for any such thinking will be a mockery—he needed to lean on tradition, and on authority and example which he could respect. Should he have had that in the years before his teenage —when he must indeed begin to think for himself—then he comes to that age strengthened and in a measure prepared. But your era no longer has the instinct out of which it can give him that. I am here to tell you that it must look now to another source than instinct.

If he has had that boon, as some few, of course, still have, then he will indeed begin after puberty to pass his own judgments on the world about him, but he will not simply refuse to listen to all who judge differently. As it is today, let us suppose he does listen occasionally—what does he hear? What does he hear in the talk that goes on in his family, what does he hear when he turns on the radio, or read when he opens a newspaper? He hears only the chaotically conflicting judgments of an adult world which is, at bottom, in the same predicament as himself. He has just tumbled, as it were, into a deep dry gulf between thought and instinct, which were formerly one within him, and there is no help for him, because the world into which he is awakening is in that very same gulf. Neither his teachers, if he still has any, nor any other adult companions can help him to bridge the gulf, because they have as yet found no bridge themselves. Now that instinct itself no longer affords a bridge, they know of no way to and fro across the void that yawns between an impotent thinking emancipated from instinct on the one side, and, on the other, a dehumanized instinct emancipated from thought.

I begin to perceive what you mean, said Burgeon. All that you said before applies with double force to the adolescent because, by virtue of his own stage of development, he is so to speak in the thick of it. He is the age *in* the age. In fact, we might say that adolescence bears rather the same relation to the Michael age as biology did to the Gabriel age.

You put things very neatly, said the Meggid dryly. What, he added gently, after a long pause, are you going to do?

Do?

Do with all this information.

You will tell me that, too, I expect.

No, said the Meggid, that is your affair when you are on your feet each day. That you must decide for yourself—where things are happening, and often *while* they are happening.

There are so many things that I could do!

Do not flatter yourself. Do you suppose that, if you were suddenly put into James's shoes in his youth club, you could hold your own for five minutes? What would you do—try to repeat to them what I have just been saying? You would not have the faintest idea what to do or what to say. Do you really think you have acquired all his overflowing goodwill and warmth of heart simply by hearing what I have said to you, or even by thinking that it is true? Do you imagine you are somebody?

48

There is nothing that I can do, said Burgeon.

Again it was as if the Meggid twinkled very slightly, as he replied:

You leap rather quickly from one extreme to the other, do you not! The gap between knowing and effective doing is a real gap, even when the knowing is real knowing. If it were not so, the doing would still be laced with instinct—and that is not my master's way. But it is not a hopeless gap, like the void between impotent thinking and effective doing.

But can you not help me? Can you not even *advise* me?

I, said the Meggid, can only help you to *know* more. And with that he departed as suddenly as he had come.

FIVE

Burgeon was troubled. In the days that followed he could not rid himself of the aftermath of those concluding exchanges with the Meggid. Must there not be something he ought to do? Should he, for instance, get in touch with James and try to communicate something of what he was now beginning to feel he knew? There had been the strong suggestion that, if he himself only had James's other qualities, he could indeed have made use of the wisdom that came from the Meggid. And there was great need.

But would James ever listen to him? Would he even be interested? In the end, he decided—and he was not sure whether it was funk or tact that determined it—that the time had not yet come for any attempt at communication.

Nevertheless he was troubled; and this continuing trouble was itself only part of a new development in his intercourse with the Meggid. Hitherto there had been the occasional encounters and, between them—ordinary life, during which he more or less forgot the Meggid's existence, except when he was deliberately 'testing' the information he had last received. Now it was all beginning to remain much more present to him. Indeed, it was sometimes an effort to concentrate, in forgetfulness of the Meggid, on his ordinary activities. He found himself preoccupied with problems that arose out of what he had 'heard'. So that, in a sense, the testing was going on all the time.

One of these problems was this: The evolution of human consciousness was not, as he had long been aware, the haphazard affair which it was commonly supposed to be. He had not needed the Meggid to tell him that there were forces at work beneath the surface. But it was the Meggid who had given him the only *details* he knew. And, in doing so, he had insisted that one must think not only of forces, but of the beings who stood behind them. Did this mean that one must regard evolution itself as 'guided'? Much that the Meggid had said concerning a 'Gabriel' age and its successor strongly suggested that that was so. But if there was indeed this hegemony, this 'guidance', if, for example, the transition stressed as marking the last years of the nineteenth century had been actually brought about by such guidance, if, to put it crudely, everything had proceeded 'according to plan', why was there anything to worry about? In particular what had the Meggid meant by his 'time presses'—if all was for the best in the best of all possible worlds? Besides, it all too obviously wasn't!

Burgeon made more than one attempt to get back to the fountainhead for an answer to this riddle; but the Meggid was not forthcoming. For a long time he was left unaided, till he began to wonder whether he must regard the whole episode as closed. The hope, however, that this might not be so was kept alive by an inkling he had had from his previous dealings that the Meggid, though not wholly inaccessible to specific questions, preferred to choose his own times and occasions for the most important things he had to say. Later on, he was to receive startling confirmation of this. But for the moment Burgeon was in the dark. What he did feel was—and he felt it in his bones— that he must not be impatient. Either the Meggid was there or —better get on with things in the ordinary way.

One of the things that soon came in the ordinary way was an invitation to a debate organized by a group of members from both branches of the legal profession who were interested in penal reform. The prisons were too full. There had been an unusual number of outbursts of organized violence inside them; and, outside, a young man, or boy, under twenty-one had been hanged for coolly shooting a policeman dead. There had been letters in *The Times* from judges, bishops, biologists, psychiatrists and Conservative back-benchers, in the course of which the advocates of prison reform, or of the abolition of capital punishment, were accused of sobbing sentimentally over the murderer and coldly ignoring his victim, while they in turn imputed to their opponents vindictiveness, sadism and a puerile desire to put the clock back.

The debate, which took place in the hall of one of the Inns of Court, followed pretty closely the lines of the recent correspondence in the Press. It was opened by an elderly barrister with a practice in the criminal courts. He gave some horrifying examples of the hardened types it had brought him into contact with. It was all very well to talk of rehabilitation and reform by gentle methods; he was all for that, where it could be applied; but too often you had to deal with a human being who had sunk to, or perhaps never risen above, a level at which he was totally impervious to anything of the sort. Many of those who theorized about them had never actually *met* a typical recidivist in their lives. The first duty of the law must be to protect society against violence, to protect the lonely and helpless old women who were the commonest victims of the heartless, and often pretty well mindless, thug.

It was absurd to contend that the fear of punishment did not deter. The trouble was that the sentimentalists had succeeded in making us *afraid* of punishment. As to the law's secondary purpose of benefiting the criminal himself by reforming him, he suspected that here, too, in far more instances than was commonly supposed, punishment was the necessary first step. A man who had become insensitive to all but the crudest pleasure and pain could only be helped up the first step out of the abyss by the infliction of crude pain. He believed that flogging should be reinstated for the worst crimes of violence.

If, said the next speaker, the fear of punishment was really an effective deterrent, why had not crime been stamped out of civilized societies long ago? There had been enough of it in the bad old days, but wretches who knew they might be hanged for it had still gone on stealing sheep. What kept the emphasis on punishment alive was not the desire to deter. It was the desire for retaliation—vengeance, in fact. Vengeance never got anyone anywhere, and he had thought—until he had heard a man, for whom he entertained as much respect as he did for the last speaker, advocate flogging—that the men of goodwill had at last really learnt this lesson. Lawyers more than any other men should be in a position to know that the concept of punishment went back to the *lex talionis*—an eye for an eye, and a tooth for a tooth. He referred to the Howard League. In the long run society would benefit more from helping the criminal than from hurting him. It was true that reform, especially the first steps, presented great difficulties in the worst cases, but the difficulties should not be avoided as a red light but accepted as a challenge.

The debate continued. Magistrates were alternately praised and rebuked for the increasing use they made of probation orders and for their habit of admonishing and binding over young hoodlums who were laughing at them all the time up their sleeves. The two sides never really seemed to meet. Burgeon became aware that the division between them corresponded roughly with a political divergence, the emphasis on punishment coming from Conservative speakers and the emphasis on reform and therapy from the Socialists. He caught the chairman's eye and found himself on his feet.

He endeavoured to expound a more Aristotelian concept of 'retribution' and to distinguish it carefully from the Roman and Jewish one of retaliation. The latter was aimed at satisfying the outraged feelings of the victim or his relatives; but retribution was a satisfaction which society itself, as such, demanded; and that was a demand which it might well prove health-giving for the criminal to have to meet. A time might come when it would be superseded, when retribution would be wholly transformed into a conscious and deliberate healing by the community of their weaker brother. But he doubted if that time was yet. A generation, which to a large extent did not even *believe* in the soul, could hardly claim to have won the wisdom out of which to set about healing it. Meanwhile there was a deep feeling for retribution—a feeling quite distinguishable from the vindictiveness which often did, but which might or might not, accompany it—an instinctive feeling that might perhaps have some of that very wisdom latent within it, a feeling that often expressed itself quite simply as a judgment about what was 'fair' and what was 'not fair'. He would vote against the motion to preserve punishment, but he would do so in spite, rather than because, of most of the arguments he had heard against it. He ended by suggesting that to tell a man frankly you were punishing him because he had done wrong showed a fundamentally deeper respect for his dignity than to tell him you were curing him because there was something wrong with him. It could involve the whole difference between treating him as a subject—a responsible human being— and treating him as a mere object.

He was startled by the virulent contempt with which the next speaker dismissed his contribution to the debate: No wonder we lawyers were accused of splitting hairs! The speaker saw no difference whatever between retribution and retaliation; resort to pitiful casuistry of that kind merely showed that the flog 'em and hang 'em brigade were not only on the defensive but in the last ditch; he congratulated the previous speaker on the gift which he was handing these gentry on a plate, to enable them to indulge their sadistic appetites and their consciences both at the same time, while sheltering themselves—if he had heard correctly—under the comforting umbrella of Aristotle. A typically English picnic! (*Laughter.*) After which he lowered his tone and delivered a speech which, it seemed to Burgeon (but perhaps he was prejudiced), did not add anything new to what had been said two or three times already.

The following speaker believed he might be able to pour a little oil on the troubled waters. Feelings, he suggested, ran high because minds were confused, not necessarily through any fault of their own. The whole dispute had been inextricably tangled up (and in this connection he referred to Burgeon's concluding remarks) not only in this room but everywhere else where it was argued, not only today but at all times in the past, by the pseudo-concept of 'responsibility'. True, English jurisprudence had at last brought itself to admit that there could be such a thing as 'diminished' responsibility, but English jurisprudence was still, as usual, about a hundred years behind the times. The plain fact was that no one abreast of modern philosophy—still less any really contemporary psychiatrist—worked any longer with the notion of personal responsibility at all. That notion originated in the unconscious mind, where the animism of our primitive fore-bears still survived. Once this was properly understood, we should grow out of the religious, or superstitious, habit of look-ing on the criminal as a kind of 'sinner'; but we should also—and he turned to a previous speaker—give up indignantly accusing the *non*-criminals in the community of similar sins of vindictive-ness, sadism and the like. The latter were, after all, merely projecting on to the criminal their fears of their own suppressed criminal impulses—which we all shared. He mentioned the scapegoat. All this had been proved long ago. Once it became generally accepted, the problem would stand revealed as the relatively simple one it, in fact, was, namely to determine scientifically the causes which brought it about that A com-mitted a crime, while B and C did not—and then to remove them. He agreed that this might take some time. But it had the advantage of being the only way which could not fail . . .

And in due course the motion: That this house deplores the current tendency to substitute reform for punishment as the guiding principle in the treatment of convicted felons, was put to the vote and passed by a small majority.

Something was puzzling him; and it was not as yet very clearly defined. He sat trying to focus it in his mind's eye and get it into a perspective which would render at least its outlines apparent. At last they began to emerge from their vague obscurity. It was a sort of psychological progress from warm feeling, through thought, into bitterness and cold. Why had some of the speakers in that debate, and particularly those who opposed the motion, developed that touch of acidity? They wanted to do away with the barbarity of organized reprisal and presumably, somewhere in the depths, it was compassion that was moving them. It was the same compassion that had led him to vote against the motion himself. The naïve intellectual complacency of the speaker who had followed him, though it had done more harm than good to the cause he was supporting, did not alter the facts. Indeed, when he strongly imagined the kind of influence to which young people brought up in tough surroundings were subjected almost from babyhood, he found himself wavering a little. *Would* it be better to abandon the concept of responsibility altogether? But in any case why the asperity? Why was the quality of mercy so often so conspicuously strained? Why did the champions of gentleness in human dealing tend to turn so *nasty* when anyone ventured to disagree with them?

Well, he had succeeded in focusing the phenomenon at last, and in the act of doing so he realized that it was not one which he was approaching for the first time. He was not cognizing, he was *recognizing* it. Where, then, had he come across it before? It was some little time before, casting about in his memory, he hit upon the answer.

There was that young Communist. Burgeon recalled a conversation with the boy some years back, when his thoughts were first beginning to turn towards the Party. Raw with compassion he had been for the miseries of the poor and deprived, which he had encountered at first hand, though he had not personally suffered them, and burning with generous indignation at the supine complacency of the privileged. Burden had tried to dissuade him from the step he contemplated. After all, he had said, there were others who felt these things, too. 'Yes, but you don't *do* anything!' the boy had cried, and Burgeon had found no satisfactory answer.

Recently he had met him again, a hardened fellow traveller; not actually a Party member, because his allotted task was to remain tin he institution where he earned his living and undermine it by creating discontent, disaffection and distrust. He now talked like the *Daily Worker* and, as far as Burgeon could make out, regarded lying and fraud as legitimate instruments and probably the best ones for attaining the Party's ends. Probe as he would, Burgeon could find no trace of the pristine compassion; the indignation remained, but the generosity had vanished from it. The youth was as energetic as ever, but he had become an out-and-out cynic, energized principally by hate. It was the same phenomenon—or rather the same noumenon. For how could this that he was thinking about possibly be called a phenomenon? It was not a *behaviour* he was recognizing—that had been quite different in the two cases. It was what lay behind it. What he was thinking about was non-physical. But that kind of thinking was exactly what—and suddenly he became aware that the Meggid was with him.

For some time now, said the Meggid, you have been asking a question which I have not answered. Now I will do so.

Your question has been: If the evolution of the earth and of humanity is in any sense guided by spiritual beings more powerful than man, why does it not proceed smoothly to an appointed end? So far, I have omitted nearly half the picture. If there have been, and are still, the good guides, as I will call them, there have also been, and are still, other immaterial beings more powerful than man—their opponents, whom men rightly experience as evil.

The devil! said Burgeon promptly.

In this Michael age, went on the Meggid sternly, the time has come to realize clearly what has hitherto only been dimly divined here and there—that there are two different kinds, two opposing hosts, of such beings, or, if you will have it so, two devils. Both of them are opponents of man's true evolution, but they are also opposite to each other. One of them works in all that fosters warmth of soul; the leading characteristic of the other—and he is the one whose presence you have just now accurately detected—is coldness. The Meggid hesitated: Once again—names are a necessity. The one who works through

warmth and light you may think of as Lucifer. As to the other—
he has been called by many names. He has been called the Prince
of this World. He has been called Satan. He has been called
Mephistopheles. But perhaps . . . in my own case, you deliberately chose an unfamiliar name, and you were right to do so.
The Persians named the Regent of cold and darkness Angri-
Manu, or Ahriman, and that is the name I choose. Whatever
name you will call him by, you have just found him by identifying
his one energy in two different places. But they are only two out
of how many! When your eyes are opened, you will find him, as
you will find Lucifer also, at work everywhere; at once in the
mind and body of man and in the earth whereof that body is part.

You spoke of their being opposite to each other. Do they,
then, actively oppose each other as well as opposing *us*? Are they
enemies?

It is for you to make them so, once you have been alerted to
their presence. And it is for this Michael age, with its new level
of self-awareness, to *be* so alerted. Otherwise it will decline
increasingly into chaos. And from chaos into worse than chaos.
That is why Ahriman discourages belief in his own existence—
and indeed in Lucifer's. And how skilfully he succeeds!

Can there be a worse than chaos?

It will decline into an organized subhumanity—a well-knit
unity in which there are no longer any individual men, but only
separate bodily mechanisms. But you need not look so far ahead.
I must answer your question. Lucifer and Ahriman are opposite
to each other inasmuch as they impinge from opposite directions.
Detected and understood, they may be balanced against each
other in such a way that both of them will work in the psyche as
rightful energy. Undetected they *co-operate*, all the more
intricately, all the more subtly, because of the opposite directions
from which their impulses come. It is this that enables them to
play so skilfully into one another's hands in their joint exploita-
tion of humanity.

But this is too generalized to help you much. I am telling it to
you now because your mind has been resting on two examples of
that very co-operation. Pity—compassion—is a warm impulse;
and therefore Lucifer can find a home in it, twisting it a little out
of the true. Can you find an example of what I mean?

There was Dostoevsky's Grand Inquisitor, said Burgeon. Am
I right in thinking of him?

There it was twisted a long way out of the true. But you are right. It is the mode and the direction of the distortion that you must grasp. Into that distortion, however slight—into the crack, as it were, as soon as it has opened—enters swiftly Ahriman, to exploit it in his quite opposite way. It is for him to distort the thinking which seeks, by removing its causes, to remedy the distress that aroused compassion in the first place. He sees to it, if he can, that the compassion is first alloyed, then debased, and then suppressed and forgotten.

I think I begin to see. It is intolerable to hold responsible for his crimes a human being who has never been taught to think that they *are* crimes, who has perhaps even been encouraged as a child to pursue them as virtues. And therefore Ahriman—

The true gods, said the Meggid, do not use the word intolerable. They say it is piteous. It is Lucifer who says it is intolerable, and then it is Ahriman who skilfully leads this abhorrence over into—

—into defining responsibility itself as a 'pseudo-concept', Burgeon interrupted. We begin with the impulse to heal instead of to punish—and we end in reckless physiological tamperings, with a monolithic State to enforce submission to them.

You will end there, *unless* you learn to recognize Lucifer and Ahriman when you see them.

But what of the Marxist? We have left him out.

Ahriman is cold. From cold calculation to cold hate is all too short a step. But come, we must look farther afield. I would not have you think that Ahriman and Lucifer are only significant in a sociological context. Now that, in however narrow a corner, you have recognized one of them for yourself, there is more, much more, that I can tell you of both. It will still be little enough of all there is to tell. So far I have spoken of warmth and cold, of light and darkness; but you must consider also the relation of these beings to time, that is, to evolution as a whole.

I said I would listen without prejudice and I cannot accept that those two concepts are identical.

Time, without change, is indistinguishable from eternity. Do not accept what I say. Think further of it. In any case what I have *now* to say does not depend on it. The aim of Lucifer is to conserve the past too long; to maintain, in the present, conditions that rightly obtained in the past, but should now be superseded. He adores tradition. In particular he seeks to maintain the permeation of the mind by the 'given', the physical, the instinctive warmth, which men bring with them from the past and must indeed use, but which should no longer permeate, or at least not involuntarily, their mental powers. You and I, my friend, have watched him at work already, for we have seen him trying to preserve into your time the psychology and the social patterns of the Gabriel age.

And what is the function, or the aim, of Ahriman?

You must distinguish the function from the aim. It is the aims of both beings that we are at present concerned with. Their aim is to oppose those whom it will suffice for the present to call the true gods; but their *function* is to serve these gods against their will, and by means of that very opposition. Do not take this lightly, or repeat it glibly. The aim of Ahriman is to anticipate the future, precociously; to bring about, long before their appointed time, conditions which, if all goes well, will rightly obtain in the future, but which can only appear in the present as a wicked caricature. In pursuit of this aim he will persuade you, if he can, to eradicate the past instead of transforming it. He abhors tradition. History is his bane. He operates, in the present age, principally in the field of mind, leaving the feelings for Lucifer to exploit. He freezes. His purpose is to destroy everything in human thinking which depends on a certain warmth, to replace wonder by sophistication, courtesy by vulgarity, understanding by calculation, imagination by statistics.

I know him well now, said Burgeon, and how often I meet him! But I am in this difficulty. Did you not say—when we were speaking of Lawrence—that everything in human thinking that depends on a certain warmth *must* be eradicated in—in this Michael age?

The warmth must spring from a different source. It must be begotten in the heart by the logos, but by the logos in the mind, no longer directly by the logos in the physique. Ahriman, if he had his way, would freeze the thought utterly before there is time for that to happen, and in order to prevent it happening. But you are right in what you have divined. Ahriman is both the peculiar opponent and the peculiar underling of Michael. He is in truth the dragon underneath the Archangel's feet.

Burgeon remained silent for a long time. At last he took courage to raise another objection. Just now, he said, you seemed to speak as if time were almost indistinguishable from evolution;

and when I ventured to object, you replied that time without *change* is indistinguishable from eternity. Do you wish me to infer that all change is evolution?

For questions of this kind, answered the Meggid, you do not need my help. You can very well elucidate them for yourself.

The word 'evolution', said Burgeon, feeling his way as best he could, seems to imply a certain *kind* of change. Let me call it 'metamorphosis'—or rather 'transformation'—since I am rather tired of the other word. Perhaps I should think that all real change *is* transformation; and that any other kind is either mere motion—which is at least a change of position—or substitution?

There was nothing to indicate that the Meggid disapproved, so he continued: And that a transformation, as distinct from a substitution, indicates the uninterrupted presence of something common to both the old form and the new—an interior, perhaps, which is anterior to them both?

That is elementary, said the Meggid. Transformation is either a decay and death or a birth and growth.

I see, too, continued Burgeon doggedly, that, where there is a *total* transformation, the interior which persists must be of a different nature from the exterior which is transformed; where, for instance, there is a total transformation of material elements, the persisting interior, must itself be immaterial. Otherwise it would not *be* transformation, but substitution.

It is not my task, said the Meggid aloofly, to bandy the discourse by means of which the blind infer that there are also things that can be seen. My task—

But may it not, persisted Burgeon boldly, be simply a *pattern* that persists?

Come, said the Meggid, *you* are not blind, but only ignorant. My task is to teach you to recognize and name the contours of the interior which you already dimly see, that is, the beings of whom it consists.

Perhaps, said Burgeon, it is just the desire of avoiding such a recognition, perhaps it is even the fear of such a recognition, which has made the word 'pattern' so popular of late. And there is *Gestalt*, too. And I can think of some others. We glimpse a countenance, and we say hurriedly: 'Yes, that is indeed a face, but it is the face of nobody.'

That is true. And, as recognition grows more unavoidable, the struggle to evade it will grow more desperate, the verbal subterfuges more trivial. Remember this, when you are discouraged by all you hear and see around you. And ponder deeply these thoughts which I leave with you now as a viaticum: Evolution is the process by which a past form, or a past condition, is transformed into a future one. Lucifer seeks to preserve the past from dissolution; Ahriman to destroy it utterly and substitute his own invention; Michael to transform it through death and rebirth.

PART TWO

SIX

For a long, long time the Meggid remained silent. Once again Burgeon began to wonder if he had heard the last of him. He grew restless and, in spite of his resolution, impatient. Though he never felt that it was much more than a name, or the suggestion for a name, that he had taken from Karo, he turned to the book again in a mood of nostalgia, which he knew was unseemly. In Karo's case, he was reminded, not only had the Meggid's utterances continued over a much longer period, not only had they been more frequent than in his own, but they had sometimes taken a more palpable form. It was recorded that, besides the inaudible voice which was his commonest manifestation, the Meggid had even, at times, spoken aloud, using Karo's own voice, when he was in conversation with others. In spite of himself Burgeon felt humiliated. How slight the parallel! How little he himself could claim!

He continued, however, to rouse himself from such unhealthy reflections. Did he, after all, particularly *want* to set up as a sort of rival to Karo? Such an idea only needed to be entertained to be vigorously repudiated. Much better consider dispassionately what more, if anything, he could do, supposing that the Meggid had, in fact, finished with him. He resolved to work on that assumption and—well, if it should prove false, so much the better!

He had received much by way of information. There remained the task (and this had been emphasized by his informant) of meditation. He had already followed the Meggid's parting injunction by pondering deeply the three sentences of his 'viaticum'. But clearly, if he meant to proceed systematically, there was much more that he could do. He could, for instance, work out for himself its application to the particular problem which had been the occasion of the last encounter. And he could endeavour to knit together more closely than he had yet done the *whole* of what he had so far received from the Meggid.

The former of these tasks it did not take him long to fulfil. That is, it did not take him long to get as far as, with his limited knowledge and total lack of practical experience, he felt was open to him. Penology was not a topic on which he was ever likely to become dogmatic; but he did find himself firmly convinced that the principle of 'evolution', as he had now learned to see it, must apply here, too. As to the concept of 'punishment', the impulse to cling on to it in its old form—including perhaps his own fear of the abyss which opened before any drastic step towards refusal to hold the criminal responsible for his crime—this was an impulse in which he saw that Lucifer was intermeddling. The rush to the opposite extreme, the headlong plunge into that very abyss, concealed as naïve jargoning about 'the pseudo-concept of responsibility', stood out clearly as the adroit manipulation by Ahriman of the opportunity handed to him by his fellow adversary.

So much for the diagnosis. But what was the remedy? What was the positive conclusion? It was here that Burgeon acutely felt his own limitations. He could see no farther than the very general, the very difficult principle which must surely somehow be applied. 'Punishment' as such must go. Perhaps not too precipitately, perhaps not yet, but it must go. On the other hand, there must be no brusque substitution for it of 'treatment', as treatment was understood in the light of contemporary physiological and psychological sciolism. The 'healing' that should one day take the place of punishment must be a true transformation; so that a future generation would be able to look at it and say: In this form, the form *now* taken by the community's response to its injurious members, into this form the old form, 'punishment', has died and been reborn; in this new form punishment has died into life. That was as far as he cared to take it and it was vague enough. Perhaps others . . . ?

The second elaboration was a longer, because a more difficult and complex one. There were hesitations, advances, retreats, and again advances, before he reached anything approaching a settled state of mind. He began by recapitulating all he could remember concerning the nature of evolution in general. By recalling his exchanges with the Meggid on this topic, and on the further point to which it had led, concerning the anterior *sine qua non* for any transformation or metamorphosis, he first sharpened, as it were, the light in which he had now learned to see these processes, and then sought to shed that light back upon the material of the earlier encounters. The formation of the brain structure, of which the Meggid had spoken, must itself be an example of evolution. There was the immaterial transforming agent, first entering as it were into the old form, and then withdrawing from it when it had become the new; for had he not spoken of those forces that were 'set free', once maturity had been attained? And was not this the very 'dying into life' of which transformation consisted? Burgeon tried not to stop there. He must assume, if he were to conduct the test properly, that the two adversaries were also at their work and he must ask himself what form their opposition would take. Clearly Lucifer's aim would have been to preserve the old form unaltered from generation to generation, to nullify, in fact, the whole purpose of the transforming agent. And Ahriman's? *He* would hasten the extinction of the old form, if he could; but he would see to it that the new form, which replaced it, was no longer the creation of the transforming agent, but some caricatured invention of his own—something harder, something *pre*-mature. Between them they would seek to eliminate the transforming agent altogether.

Along this line of thought, however, he soon found he could progress no farther. He did not know enough about it. He had, of course, no proof that any such process had been going on. If it had been, and if the two adversaries had, in fact, worked in the way he was supposing, it seemed they had failed. For the Meggid had spoken as though *this* transformation at least had been successfully accomplished. He had spoken as of a process of biological evolution. Perhaps in the case of biological evolution, if the two adversaries were indeed at work (and the Meggid had expressly said that they were active in nature as well as in man), the struggle to keep them at bay, or rather to hold the balance between them, was outside man's province altogether.

Burgeon decided that he at any rate must leave nature alone and confine himself to spotting the working of the two adversaries in the mind of man. As to evolution— Good heavens! He suddenly saw in a blinding light what they *had* done—not indeed with biological evolution itself, but with the picture men had formed of that evolution. The picture they had induced us to form was one of a cosmic process in which *nothing but* Lucifer and Ahriman were at work; of a process which they and they alone could have brought about! It was a process of transformation, from which *transformation itself* had been eliminated! Men spoke of evolution and described—a succession of substitutions. They had found 'heredity' at its work of preserving the old form unaltered—for it was easy to find Lucifer—and they had found 'environment' repeatedly destroying the old, to substitute an adventitious new—for it was still easier to find Ahriman. Between the two they had crushed out the transforming agent altogether. A few lone voices like those of Goethe, Agassiz, G. H. Schubert, the biologist, had been raised in protest, but they had been quickly drowned. The adversaries themselves had seen to that. This, then, was the picture we were left with—the two opposing influences so clearly seen, the two sides of the canvas so delicately painted—and the central figure, which alone gave meaning to them, omitted! It was like—it was like—it was like —and he found himself striving to imagine what manner of picture Leonardo da Vinci's *Last Supper* would be with the central figure blacked out of it.

Burgeon calmed down for a moment. Well, it was a false picture. And what of it? What did it matter, since it could not affect the process itself? But what if we were approaching a point, as some maintained, at which biological evolution and the evolution of consciousness were becoming indistinguishable? If the transforming agency were indeed being delivered into the hands of man himself? Was that what the Meggid had meant by his 'Michael age'? How if the picture which man formed, the memory he embodied, of his own past deeds, were henceforth to *be*, in some way, the transforming agent? If precisely *that* had been the 'fertilization' of which the Meggid had spoken at that very first encounter? And if anything, which was *not* that, could be only Luciferic induration, interrupted by Ahrimanic substitutions and replacements?

At this point he realized that he was going too fast. That possibly Coleridgean, but still excessive, 'esemplastic' tendency of his! It had waltzed his imagination from biological to psychological evolution as if there were no distinction between them. True, others had long been engaged in bridging the same gap in their own way. There was the 'emergent' evolution of the evolutionary biologists, who thought with Julian Huxley, and there was Teilhard de Chardin's variant of it. But this was hardly what his imagination had intended. Clearly he must pause and consider again the precise quarry he was tracking down.

If you started from the fact that evolution was the transformation of a past into a present, what followed? In what sense was human consciousness already, not merely the *result*, but a transformation, of the remote past which interested the biologists? He had seen, he believed, the falsity of the nineteenth-century picture of that past and he now had an inkling of how and why that picture had arisen and fastened itself on the Western mind. Moreover, thanks to the Meggid, he could now rule out the corollary to this vacuous heredity/environment picture of evolution—the persistent assumption that an originally mindless universe had somehow generated mind. But he had still to admit that a universe devoid of individual minds *had* somehow generated individual minds. This was the gap he had leaped too readily, permitting himself to equate personal memory with some kind of stored experience of the human race as a whole.

At this point some earlier studies he had made of the history of language—and a long habit of reflection and meditation on its nature and origin—stood him in good stead. As to its nature, language was, for him, an outstanding example of the past surviving, transformed, in the present. The commonly received 'tool' theory, which was now being applied to both its origin and its nature, vanished, of course, with that same chimera of an originally 'mindless' universe. On the contrary, you had to see the origin of language as the self-gathering of mind within an already mind-soaked world. It was the product of 'nature' in the sense that the meanings of words, if you approached them historically, could all—or as nearly all as made no difference—be shown to be involved with natural phenomena. Moreover, interfusion of the sensuous (sound) with the immaterial (meaning) was still, even today, its whole point. Yet it was certainly not, in its earlier stages, the product of *individual* minds; for it was obviously already there at a stage of evolution when individual minds were not yet. He had no doubt of its pointing back to a state of affairs when men and nature were one in a way that had long since ceased. Even now, even in our own time, there was the mysterious 'genius of language' which many philologists had detected as something that worked independently of any conscious choices. On the other hand, you could see that, as time went on, language did come to owe more and more to the working of individual minds. However you looked at it, you could not get away from the fact that every time a man spoke or wrote there was this intricate interfusion of past and present—of the past transformed, as meaning, with the present impulse behind his act of utterance.

Then, as to the history of language, it had always seemed to him to be the key to history itself. He recalled the late birth (upon his realizing this) of his own interest in history, which at school had somehow passed him by. It was a different matter altogether when you saw that history was still immanent, still present, in so many words in everyday use. Incidentally it had always seemed to him that this was where Oswald Spengler had gone astray. His picture of a series of successive civilizations each starting afresh from scratch left out the seed-corn of language.

In this light it seemed proper, it seemed inevitable, to Burgeon to regard human history—with all its numberless variations on the central theme—as a single process, which could properly be called the transformation of human consciousness. And he could include, for this purpose, in the term 'history' both pre-history and the evolution that had preceded it. And now suppose one assumed—and he was strongly inclined to do so—that it was this very perspective, this very way of looking at the past, to which the human mind was at present in the act of awakening for the first time! What followed? At first, confusion. Confusion was not only very probably to be expected, it was inevitable. After all, what happened when you awoke from your own dreams? An analogy perhaps, but a true and significant one; because dreams are the half-way stage from the unindividualized consciousness of sleep to the vigilant watch and ward of waking day. Dream-consciousness was characterized by the absence of the central, controlling agent—or rather by its incipient return to control. And how often it took the form, precisely, of fantastic and illusory explanations of the awakening impact itself! The dispersal of these illusions, as slumber receded, differed sharply from the wakeful correction of wakefully entertained errors. In that case the same person, who had committed the error, afterwards corrected it. But it was a transformed person who suddenly abandoned the dream. He abandoned it because he was transformed. And he could now look back on the dream and see it for what it was—a dream. There was often a stage, moreover, in this process, where choice entered in. The slumber-laden mind could either voluntarily relapse into the dream—or it could choose to become itself the transforming agent and conclude the process of waking itself up.

It seemed to him a fair analogy. After all, the very idea of transformation was only a few centuries old. It was hard indeed on the human mind that *the moment at which it first began to entertain the idea of transformation should also be the moment at which it was itself in the act of becoming the transforming agent*! No wonder if it had failed, as yet, to understand. No wonder if it was still looking desperately round outside for that which it was itself just beginning consciously to be. A golden opportunity indeed for the two adversaries—for Lucifer to keep mankind still dreaming, if he might; for Ahriman to startle them, as with an electric shock, into the cockney wakefulness that forgets it has ever dreamed at all, that denies any identity between a waking and dreaming self, that repudiates those wells of sleep from which it drew the very strength it now enjoys as vigilance!

SEVEN

At about this time Burgeon reached the age at which he could retire from his profession; and he decided to employ the increment of leisure, which thus became his portion, in pursuing as systematically as he could the whole line of enquiry that had now been opened to him. Whether or not it should lead to anything, and whether or not he was to be favoured with any further communications from the Meggid, it would, he decided, be the best way of doing what he had always hoped to do after his retirement, namely reading.

One of the disadvantages of living in the twentieth century is that, on almost any subject, there is too much reading matter available. He had long ago discovered that the only fruitful way of ploughing a furrow through the plethora was to be in pursuit of some particular quarry. It was like dipping a thread into a liquid containing crystals in solution. The crystals gathered round the thread. You selected ruthlessly, but in the process of selection you read much, you read swiftly, and your mind was alert. What you did not retain you were nevertheless more alive to than you would otherwise have been; what you did retain you digested.

He had no doubt about *his* thread, though it would have been difficult to name it. Throughout the pre-history and the history of humanity there was, on the one hand, a process of evolution going forward, about which it was difficult to know very much; and, on the other hand, there was the picture which men themselves eventually formed of this process, the picture, in fact, which they formed of their own past. There was firstly the actual transformation as it had gone on through the ages; and there was, secondly, the prevailing picture of this transformation—the picture of a purely biological process with the transforming agent omitted. Thirdly, in the case of the recent transition from a Gabriel to a Michael age, there were, on the one hand, all the

72

unconscious, or half-conscious processes which he had seen so clearly with the help of the Meggid; and on the other hand there was—what? Not only no picture, but not even a theory. Not only no theory, but hardly even a dim perception of one. Only a whirl of uneasiness that *betrayed* something of what had occurred without even beginning to account for it.

It did appear that, when you came to the evolution of *consciousness*—and this was the quarry he was really after—the distinction between the two elements—the process itself and men's awareness of the process—was less easy to maintain. For here the awareness was itself an important part of the *res*, perhaps the most important part. At least, that must be so if, as he had come to believe, it was precisely into an awareness of its own past that human consciousness was in the act of 'awakening'.

Clearly, then, he must somehow get to know much more than he did about history. For history *was* the awakening of man to at least an *interest* in his own past; and it was an awakening which had really only begun three or four hundred years ago. It was only since then, and only in the West, that history had been approached as in any sense a *process*. And here the crystal-gathering thread, the ruthless selection, began to operate. There was altogether too much history. According to Toynbee, for instance, there were twenty-one different civilizations to be studied, if one were not to acquire a parochial outlook based only on one's own, or on that and a couple of others. But then what *he* was interested in was the 'awakening'. He would very much have liked to know all available history, but since it was the awakening he was concerned with, he must confine himself a good deal to the history of that civilization which had itself begun to study history; and, parochial or not, that was his own western European civilization. Perhaps Toynbee himself had not seen just how sharply this particular civilization was distinguished from the other twenty by the fact that the other twenty had contained no Toynbees!

Lastly, in addition to the vast accumulation of histories over the last two centuries, there was the much more recent philosophical interest in the *nature* of history. There were those who, like himself, were deeply concerned not only with the past of men but with what that concern itself signified. This surely must be the very growing-point of the 'awakening'. It was with all this in mind that Burgeon dipped into Bachofen and read (*inter alia*)

Berdyaev's *Meaning of History* and Collingwood's *Idea of History*—Collingwood, who had so valiantly defended the startling proposition that 'all history is the history of thought'.

So it came about that, unassisted by the Meggid, he spent the first year of his retirement in studying—or perhaps 'raiding' would be a less presumptuous term—the history of Western thought and making many discoveries in the process—one of which was that the history of dogma had played a far more important part in it than he had hitherto supposed.

But there was another strand in his thread, which was hardly less important than the one that has been mentioned. Nothing from his intercourse with the Meggid had left a deeper impression on him than that disclosure of the part played by the two adversaries. He never lost sight of this and he was astonished by the repeated vestiges he found of their chronic influence in eliminating men's awareness of the immaterial transforming agent and, where possible, eliminating the operation of the transforming agent itself. He thought he detected how, as time went on, these two endeavours merged increasingly into one and the same.

Russians, if their novels and some travellers are to be believed, are almost always ready to discuss first things with one another. They wear their *Weltanschauungs* on their sleeves, so to speak. The English for the most part only do that when they are young. This is perhaps not so phlegmatic as it sounds. For one thing, if you take your view of the world seriously, to air it is tiring. Moreover, in any ordinary conversation you can only do so very superficially and your own heard superficiality wounds you. The opinions, whether firm or tentative, of a man over fifty who has thought for himself about the nature of man and the universe will have acquired a certain depth and weight that make them ill adapted for point-blank encounter. Submarines rarely engage one another directly in battle.

Occasionally, however, an exceptional combination of circumstances may lead to such an engagement. When, about eighteen months after his retirement, Burgeon was on a voyage to South Africa to visit some relations, he gradually became more and more aware of the pleasing identities of two fellow passengers. Casual encounters on deck or in the smoking-room led, after three days, to their addressing one another by name, and the habit grew on them of foregathering at odd times. In the course of the usual exchanges covering the purpose of the voyage, the home background which had led to it and incidental topics, it became apparent that they were all three fairly wide readers and the field of discourse was gradually and agreeably extended. Burgeon had discovered by this time that Chevalier was a Roman Catholic.

The actual occasion, however, which brought on the two conversations relevant to this chronicle did not occur until they were only three days out of Cape Town. Grimwade and Chevalier, entering the smaller smoke-room, found Burgeon alone there with Somervill's Abridgment of Toynbee's *Study of History*.

'I'm interested to see,' said Grimwade after they had both sat down, 'that you are one of the very small company who actually *read* Toynbee. I meet all sorts of people who talk about him without having read him, and I suppose I have done it myself.'

'They all drag in Toynbee,' said Chevalier. 'They can't leave him alone. And, as you say, hardly any of them have read him.'

There was a silence, and Burgeon felt that something was due from him. 'Well,' he said, 'I am glad I have joined the great minority. As a matter of fact, I am really interested in his theory of history.'

'And do you accept it?' asked Chevalier.

Looking back on it afterwards, Burgeon realized that this had been the turning-point. The question was asked casually, almost for something to say, certainly without any intention of 'starting' anything. He could have turned it off in the same way with an 'Oh, I don't know!' or an 'In some ways, perhaps', and a year ago that is what he would have done. But Burgeon, too, was evolving. He closed his eyes and repeated the question to himself. And then:

'At least,' he said slowly, 'Toynbee divines some kind of immaterial agency at work in it. It's about time somebody did.'

'He picks out his pattern,' said Chevalier. 'But I should have thought a good many people had been doing that, ever since the anthropologists first got to work. It's becoming almost a parlour game.'

'I feel it's rather more than that somehow. You asked me if I accepted Toynbee's theory. Well, no. I don't. But I wouldn't go so far as to say there is no value in it—as I gather you do.'

'No,' said Chevalier, 'I wouldn't say that either. His theory

75

gives him a deeply felt "point of view". And it seems to have
been proved by experience that an historian without a point of
view can only be a dull historian. If that was true of the less
pretentious histories people used to write—people like Grote
or Froude or Macaulay—I suppose we oughtn't to complain if
it's turning out to be true of the so-called world histories as well.'

'That "point of view" business is all very well,' said Burgeon.
'But it seems to me that, carried to its logical conclusion, what
you are really saying is that there is no such thing as history.'

'No such thing as history,' put in Grimwade cheerfully—
'only Lytton Strachey.'

'Oh no,' said Chevalier. 'History, as a record of fact, is a
science like any other, and amenable to scientific disciplines.'

'Not like any other,' objected Grimwade. 'If so, why should
it need a "point of view"? With history, except for very short
periods and very limited fields, you cannot separate the fact from
the interpretation of the fact. I defy you to do it. And even if you
do limit your objective severely in space and time, if you cut out
all interpretation, you still won't be able to produce much more
than a list of dates—a sort of register of births, deaths and
marriages—and, I suppose, battles and acts of parliament.'

'As I see it,' said Burgeon reflectively, 'there are at least three
difficulties in the way of the scientific approach to history: first,
that the raw material available is not facts, but surviving records
of facts, conflicting records very often. Interpretation is interposed from the very start. It is not facts; it is tradition that the
historian has to deal with. Secondly, when the facts concerned
are human actions, it simply makes nonsense to try and deal
with them apart from motives—or from the thought which was
involved with them. Collingwood is good on both these points.
Lastly, when it comes to remote periods—pre-history—you
haven't even got the record or the tradition. It's all unverifiable
inference from a few fossils and potsherds—with the result that
the fact and the interpretation of the fact are more inextricably
entangled than ever.'

'Still,' said Grimwade, 'it's good fun guessing.'

But Burgeon was not to be put off. 'If it's not boring you,' he
said, 'I'd like to try to work out an example of what I mean. If
you try to tackle the past scientifically, and yet to arrive at
something more than a table of dates, or a chronicle, you *must*
try to find principles of some sort underlying it. All science is

doing this all the time. Moreover, you must go on trying to reduce the principles to fewer and fewer and more and more generalized ones. You must assume that everything can be explained by x, or x + y, or x + y + z, if you could only find x, y and z. You tell yourself, for instance, that, subject to minor variations, the actions of human beings are determined by race on the one hand and environment on the other. Now you have got something to go on, and the helter-skelter begins to fall into some kind of pattern. You see the pattern everywhere, and your interpretation of the facts, or rather of the records or the tradition, you are dealing with is determined by the pattern you see.

'Now, I think Toynbee is pretty good on this. He points out the fallacy of trying to apply the methods evolved in natural science. He shows up the part which just this pattern—or point of view, if you like—the race-plus-environment one—has, in fact, played in the writing of modern histories. And he questions its adequacy. But then it seems to me he doesn't keep it up. He warns us against the fallacy of applying to historical thought, which is a study of living creatures, a scientific method devised for the study of inanimate objects. If I remember right, he calls it "the converse of the pathetic fallacy". I rather like that. But I doubt if he realizes how much of the rejected method he himself still retains—and not only the method itself but the whole set of assumptions which have come from applying the method previously.'

'Can you give an example?' asked Grimwade.

'Yes. It seems to me his central theory is an example. I don't feel that his two principles, Challenge and Response, are anything like as different from Race and Environment as he supposes. Challenge and Environment, at least in the earlier stages of his civilizations, are almost interchangeable terms. It is true that his Response is shown to be independent of racial differentiation and that it represents a kind of inner spiritual principle; but the main structure of his thought is still the structure on which nineteenth-century natural science was erected. It is a chain of causes and effects, arising from the interaction of two conflicting forces—and thus, in form, mechanistic. He criticizes H. G. Wells and others for trying to apply the race and environment pattern to later stages of human evolution, where it is obviously inadequate. But is he much better off himself—when he has to start speaking of "internal" responses to "internal" challenges arising from the respondent's own nature?'

'That,' said Chevalier, 'is the penalty for trying to detect a single pattern in a series of events which are not particularly related to one another.'

'Unless it is the penalty for fancying the wrong pattern?'

'I don't see how you can find any pattern at all if you boycott cause and effect.'

'Unless the cause-and-effect mode of thought is itself the result of the duality—of thinking always of *two* forces interacting.'

'This may become interesting,' said Grimwade. 'Go on.'

Burgeon did not find it easy to go on. He was feeling his own way, trying to penetrate further for himself rather than to convince the others. There came now into his mind the substance of his last encounter with the Meggid. 'Can I go back a little farther?' he asked. 'It seems fairly obvious to me that the reason why the duality of race and environment took such a strong hold on so many historians is this: that it is simply an application to history of another duality which had already been accepted as the basis of evolution in general: I mean *Heredity* and Environment. Toynbee's occasional allusions to pre-history suggest that he himself fully accepts this basis. But doesn't that entail that he is doing the very thing he tells us *not* to do— applying to living creatures the forms of thought adapted to inanimate objects?'

'All very well,' said Chevalier, 'but what are you going to substitute for it—except unedifying and unverifiable speculations?'

'Well, but *my* point is that you *must* substitute something for it—either substitute something else or give it up. And that is really Toynbee's point, too—at the beginning. Only, as I say, he doesn't live up to it.'

'Have *you* got anything to substitute?'

'Only this. I would say that the impulse to read history in terms of evolution is a sound one. Only one must first understand what evolution involves. And, for the reason Toynbee himself has given, this is what almost nobody does understand. Evolution is a process of transformation: and you can never understand transformation in terms of duality—in terms of the state of affairs before and the state of affairs after the transformation—the first causing the second. You can only understand it

78

in terms of an immaterial transforming agent, which is there both before and after the change.'

'Go on,' said Grimwade.

Burgeon again cast desperately about in his mind, and as he did so he again recalled the Meggid. Only this time his mind went back to the very first encounter that had surprised him on the morning after that conversation about D. H. Lawrence, the encounter that had come upon him even before he had chosen a name. He recalled the structure that had been evolving in the brain, and the manner of it—interior forces at work and their sub-sequent liberation. He knew he could not speak of this without the risk of being avoided as a crank or a lunatic, and yet it seemed to provide exactly what he wanted. For the picture of it now, at this moment, for the first time linked itself in his mind with a certain passage from Toynbee's book. 'The odd thing is,' he said at last, 'that at one point Toynbee himself comes near to saying this very thing! It comes just at the point where he tries to carry the challenge-and-response pattern farther than it will go. Or at least so I suggested just now. He is trying to show a sort of evolution or progress in the *quality* of the challenge-and-response. And he finds this in its transference to the interior realm. He says [and here Burgeon rifled through the book to the page he wanted] :

' "In this other field challenges do not impinge from outside but arise from within, and victorious responses do not take the form of surmounting external obstacles or of overcoming an external adversary, but manifest themselves in an inward self-articulation or self-determination." '

'I don't see how you get your "transforming agent" out of all that.' objected Chevalier.

'Well, no.' Burgeon still had his eyes on the page. 'I said he came *near* to saying it. But you'd have to read the whole passage. A little before, he has described the process at work as one that "liberates forces that have been imprisoned in a more material medium and thereby sets them free to work in a more ethereal medium with a greater potency".'

'I *still* don't see. It sounds to me rather like Teilhard de Chardin's "No-osphere", which is gradually going to replace the material world altogether. Though why he finds that idea so exciting, I confess I can't see. What is wrong with the material world—seeing that God made it ?'

'There is nothing wrong with the material world,' said Grimwade, 'provided you have no objection to an atomic explosion.'

'You are talking of a wrong *use* of the material world.'

'Well, perhaps it was a bad example. But how about old age and death—not to mention birth, which is not generally considered much fun for either of the parties concerned?'

'One theory, you know,' said Chevalier good-humouredly, 'is that all those woes are due to human sin.'

'Very well,' said Grimwade, 'but since we can't conceive of them without the material world in which they occur—nor conceive of a material world that includes life and consciousness, without *them*, isn't that world also due to human sin? And could you get rid of one without getting rid of the other?'

'We'd better leave that, I think—if Burgeon is to have a chance to finish.'

'If something like this "etherealization" that Toynbee advances is actually happening,' said Burgeon, 'it must be important to know about it, whether it is a good thing or a bad thing. Personally I believe something like it *is* happening and that Toynbee in his own way has twigged it. We were talking about history; and the point I was trying to make was that Toynbee is hampered in putting forward an evolutionary view of history by failing to understand the nature of evolution itself. In which failure he is admittedly in very good company. Only in his case it is particularly exasperating because (*a*) the failure is due to the very method of thought which he *says* he rejects—that is, the attempt to grasp evolution in concepts applicable only to inanimate objects, and (*b*) because in the passage from which I read he comes very near to stating the true principle.'

'The true principle being—'

'That evolution is determined from the interior. If he could have seen that this is true of *all* evolution and not only of the most up-to-date bits, he might have won through to a *really* new historical method, instead of repairs and improvements to the old one—i.e. the method of physical science transferred.'

'But isn't it his whole case—just as I believe it is Chevalier's—that this determination from the interior only comes about towards the end of the journey?'

'Yes. And that is the fallacy. Interior is—was—always anterior.'

'I don't understand you.'

'I do,' said Grimwade. 'There is a doctrine of Buddhism—you could call me a Buddhist, I suppose, only such labels mean nothing—you can't really be a Buddhist without ceasing to be *anything*—even a Buddhist! There is a principle in Buddhism known as "Mind-Only". It is *the* fundamental principle, and yet it has been lost sight of altogether in the West. When our friend Toynbee speaks of forces that are imprisoned in a more material medium and are then set free—he is talking more sense than he perhaps knows himself. He is proclaiming the root-principle of all material manifestation whatsoever. He is on to the catastrophe of birth.'

'Physical birth perhaps,' said Chevalier.

'*All* birth,' insisted Grimwade firmly.

Burgeon wondered what to do with his new ally. 'You would agree, then,' he said, 'that Toynbee is wrong in presenting this interior source of evolution as something which has itself been born—in the course of evolution!'

'Of course. It is the unborn. It is itself anterior to all births.'

'Including the births of civilizations?'

'Including the birth of time itself.'

'I'm not sure,' said Burgeon, 'that I want to get to the end quite as quickly as that. What I am really interested in is this. Granted that this interior source, from which the particular transformation that we call evolution is determined, is itself anterior to evolution, have we any sort of access to it?'

'You can't exactly say we have access to it,' said Grimwade. 'We *are* it. Access, as you call it, consists of awakening to that simple fact.'

'As a matter of fact,' said Burgeon, 'you have laid your finger there on the reason why I am interested in the current stir about philosophy of history. I have a notion that that stir is a sign that the West is beginning to awaken; to *re*awaken, if you like, to what you have just told us it had lost sight of—the immaterial agent behind all history. If so, I fancy it could lead to something like a new era—or, if you like, a new stage of evolution altogether.'

'I'm afraid,' said Chevalier, 'it is just these exciting eschatological speculations that leave me so cold.'

'I agree,' said Grimwade. 'I said nothing about "agency". And I would have thought, Burgeon, that a passionate interest in history was the worst possible preparation for awakening the mind to its own identity.'

'But why?'

'Because it imprisons the mind more firmly than ever in the illusion of time; which is the mother of *all* illusions, including the arch-illusion of its own separate existence. If you seek "access", as you call it, to the Supreme Identity, you must first lose interest in time and all that occurs in time. You must be aware that what happened at the birth of civilization is still happening, and that whatever is going to happen in your new era has happened already.'

'Unless,' said Chevalier, 'we have been saved from that very dilemma by the Timeless choosing to enter into time.'

'Yes, indeed,' said Grimwade. 'But we must remember that the Timeless is *continually* entering into time. Is not that in effect what is meant by the troublesome word "soul"? The Christian revelation was a true revelation—from the soul's point of view. It is one way by which it may awaken to its own spiritual essence. But, for spirit itself, it was an event in time like any other and on a level with any other.'

'I don't follow your distinction between soul and spirit,' said Chevalier.

'How do you know,' asked Burgeon, 'that there is no such thing as a *spiritual* event occurring in time?'

'I know it because, if that were so, there would already be multiplicity; and that is the negation of spirit. What do you mean by spirit? For all I know, there may be any number of non-physical events occurring. Everything the spiritualists say may be true. For that matter everything the Mahayana Buddhists say may be true. But the point is that it doesn't *matter*. Why should occult events be any more important than physical events? If we attend to them, they merely distract our attention from the One, which we *are*. And that was what *I* meant by "spirit". That is the difference between the perennial philosophy, which seeks the spirit, and religion, which points man *towards* it, but has to be abandoned on the way.'

'Yes,' said Chevalier. 'It is all very sublime. Would it annoy you if I said that in my opinion your claim to transcend religion is misconceived? And that your so-called Supreme Identity is simply a variant of pantheism—which is a late and decadent form of religion and not, as you calmly assume, its primitive form?'

'It wouldn't annoy me. I should merely wonder why you select a word which means finding someone called "God" everywhere as a good name for the practice of finding him nowhere.'

'I am getting giddy,' said Burgeon suddenly. 'You're trying to raise my sights too high, Grimwade. I don't know how it may be for your own. Somehow I want to get back to this business of time and timelessness. If I understand you rightly, you say it is a bad thing to be deeply interested in history, because it consists of events in time and because it is a bad thing to be deeply interested in *any* events in time.'

'If by deeply you really mean *deeply*, yes. I don't say it is a bad thing to study history intensively any more than it is a bad thing to study anything else. I let out as I did because you seemed to be suggesting something more than a harmless increase of erudition; you seemed to be suggesting that the study of history and evolution was a good way of "awakening", as I think you called it, to something beyond history. What was it you said that started us off? Interior is anterior?'

'Yes, that *was* what I said.' Burgeon paused. 'Yes . . .' he said again. 'We are to treat time itself as *maya*, and our own existence as the arch-illusion. What puzzles me is this: how do you apply the principle to your own life—which, after all, will one day be history . . . if it is not history already?'

'That is just the problem. I did not suggest that it is an *easy* principle to apply.'

'No—I am sure you didn't. What I am trying to get at is this. You affirm that the separate existence of Grimwade is an illusion —and that the sooner and the more fully Grimwade himself *realizes* this, not only in theory, but in his behaviour, too, the better it will be. Is that a fair way of putting it?'

'It will do.'

'But you agree that—at least *within* this tiresome illusion of time—there is a "problem". Grimwade does not simply withdraw from the *maya*. He fulfils his various obligations; he chooses to act in one way or another; he even thinks it worth while crossing an illusory ocean on board an illusory ship.'

'Certainly—and he tries to do it all without what he calls "attachment".'

'Yes, yes. I'm not blaming him—or trying to suggest that there is any inconsistency. All I am suggesting is that Grimwade acts on the assumption that this realization of—of himself as

83

Supreme Identity, or whatever he calls it—is, from his personal point of view, a *gradual* process. Very gradual indeed. Isn't there something called an Eightfold Path?'

'I see what you are driving at. It would take too long to go into. One would have to enter into the doctrine of Karma, for instance.'

'Reincarnation!' said Burgeon.

'No. Reincarnation is only one version of the doctrine, and in my view a corrupt one.'

'You will never persuade me,' interposed Chevalier, 'that you can have Buddhism, or any other form of Orientalism, without all the paraphernalia of pre-existence and reincarnation. Personally I believe, because it has been revealed to us, that *that* is the arch-illusion from which the Redeemer was sent to rescue us. However it may once have been, we know *now* that it is not for us to withdraw from existence.'

'If the doctrine of reincarnation is an illusion,' said Burgeon, 'it has been a very persistent one. Has not the greater part of humanity held the belief in one form or another?'

'The fact that an illusion is persistent, or even universal, does not make it any less illusory. Ask Grimwade. What about time?'

'Yes, but *you* do not regard time as an illusion!'

There was a pause. Neither Grimwade nor Chevalier seemed anxious to pursue the subject further. Chevalier got out his pipe and began filling it. And it was at this point that Burgeon became aware, for the first time since many months, of the approach of the Meggid. Together with this awareness there came a startlingly clear perception, a moment of intellectual vision which it is difficult to describe in a few words. It involved both time and space; and the whole space-time perspective, which it was, was somehow inextricably involved with what he had received from their last encounter. Perhaps it is best to formulate it first with an almost mathematical primness of generalization, leaving the reader to condemn it, or clothe it, as he thinks fit. He saw, then, the consciousness of the East, with its predominantly *cyclic* concept of time, stretching backward into the mists of antiquity and pre-history, and that of the West, with its contrasted linear concept, stretching forward into the future. So much for the generalization; and yet it did not seem one to him, because he beheld these vistas through the personalities of Grimwade and Chevalier. He saw the West striving, how vigorously, to repudiate the transformation which had brought it to birth, to expunge the past out of which it had grown, and to snap the link with its own youth, its own former being. But even more clearly than this he saw, and through a kind of lens that was Grimwade, the East struggling to preserve itself intact from the appointed transformation. Yet in the same moment he was aware, thanks to the Meggid, that it was not the West itself that was struggling to deny transformation; it was Ahriman. And it was not the East itself that was willing to defy transformation; it was Lucifer.

For Burgeon it was a pregnant moment; and yet that was not all. Something far more disconcerting followed immediately. He had intended to pursue the topic of reincarnation and had even begun to do so. 'When you use the word "reincarnation",' he was saying, when he came suddenly to a stop, forgetting how he had meant to go on. '—the *word* "reincarnation",' he repeated, with some annoyance at his own unaccountable aphasia. And then—the aphasia left him and he heard his own voice curtly treating it as an aposiopesis and continuing, with a touch of firmness that surprised him:

'But let us not consider it just now, please. There will be a time perhaps.'

It was not what he had intended to say at all; but now he went on, turning towards Grimwade as he did so:

'This is what I wanted to say about history. First, for the individual life, you *do* concede a process of gradual transformation towards spiritual awareness. It is the very path which you exhort us all to pursue. Or if *you* do not, those who think with you do. There is, for instance, a Buddhist *Society*, which must exist for some purpose—and I do not know what that purpose is, if it is not to *teach*.'

Grimwade gave some signs of being tired of the whole subject. 'Very well,' he said. 'You can put it that way. From the point of view of a soul in time. They do not teach people to *become* anything new, only to be what they are already. They learn, if they are fit for it, that we are all Brahma already—or rather have never ceased to be him.'

'But isn't that a kind of awakening? I don't mean merely accepting it in theory. You must meet plenty who do that quickly enough and then grow old and die without ever getting even a taste of the reality—is not the *actual* awakening, and do you not know that it is, a long and slow business—extending, some say, over thousands of lives?'

'I thought we weren't going to talk of reincarnation.'

'We weren't. All I am asking is, why should not what is true for the individual life be true for the history of mankind as a whole? If there is not merely an awakening, but a *process* of awakening in the one—why not also in the other?'

'If you start thinking in that way, you become still more deeply entangled with the time-illusion. It is unnecessary and therefore dangerous.'

'Yet it may be,' said Burgeon, 'that the most dangerous of all mottos for our precarious humanity is Safety First! But let us leave it at that. The second thing is this. We have agreed not to speak now of reincarnation, but that does not go for pre-existence in general. *That* you must accept as a matter of course, for everything you have contended for is based on it. It was in that context that you approved just now of Toynbee's reference to his "imprisonment" and "liberation" of forces.'

'Well?'

'It is right, is it not, that in your view the imprisonment, or something like it, occurs at birth—an imprisonment, let us say, since reference to reincarnation is out of order, of whatever it was that pre-existed, an imprisonment or darkening of what you say we *are* and always have been? May I put it that way?'

'It will do, perhaps.'

'Then, there, too, why should not the same be true of longer periods and other kinds of birth, of the birth of a civilization, of the life of humanity as a whole? It is the secret, you are convinced, of an individual's progress through time between birth and death. Why should it not also be the secret of history?'

'The secret?'

'The Jewel in the Lotus.' Burgeon now heard himself say, though the expression, he believed was new to him, 'The light into which we are gradually to awaken from our darkness.' And it was at this point that he first realized that the Meggid himself was now speaking in him. How long that had been going on, he could not say, for it was definitely 'in' and not 'through'; there was no question of his being used as a sort of microphone; and yet it was almost as much like hearing someone else speak as it was like speaking; and this because his lips were uttering, and with the confidence of personal experience, things which he must indeed have thought, but could not possibly say he *knew* from experience, since he had not lived them, or had never lived up to them—had never taken them seriously, as he took, for instance, eating and drinking seriously. Grimwade said:

'I do not think I follow the analogy.'

'Do you not? You spoke just now of this very light—you called it 'Mind-Only'—having been *lost sight* of in the West. Do you not, in fact, assume that the East once, if you go far enough back into the past, lived *in* this light? And that there has been a darkening, an imprisonment of it?'

'No. I don't. Birth has always been birth. It has always signified for all men the same old immersion in the same old illusion of individual existence. Every generation is equidistant from eternity.'

'I am afraid he is right there,' Chevalier put in.

'But in the past,' Burgeon objected, 'there still remained some *memory* of pre-existence. And, when that was gone, there still remained the tradition. Why is it that all the myths of men's origin, without exception, tell of a *descent*—a descent from some former state of happy intercourse with the gods into present exclusion from it, from a paradisal state of light and joy into an earthy one of sorrow and darkness? I defy you to find a single myth that portrays an *ascent* from unconsciousness to consciousness, from ape to man, from matter to spirit. Why not, if it was the fact? Why should those who were still near to the great change know nothing of it, report nothing of it?

'I will tell you why. It is because this *story* of a linear ascent is itself the product of the last stage of total exile from even the memory of the light—the last darkness in which there is nothing left to do but play the guessing-game with the help of the language-game. I should have thought the analogy was plain to high heaven! And if there has indeed occurred this imprisonment, this descent into the darkness of the material world—and what else is the history of Western civilization?—why may the West not work its way towards an awakening—an awakening, if you like, to what it has always been in the spirit—as you yourself say that the individual soul must do?'

Burgeon leaned back in his chair, aware that the Meggid had left him. 'I am afraid,' he said in an apologetic and faintly bewildered way, 'I have been holding forth rather!'

They both laughed. And almost at the same moment the gong

sounded for dinner. Chevalier knocked out his pipe, as Grim-wade got up and moved towards the door. Burgeon followed and Chevalier placed a hand on his shoulder as he came up behind him. 'You certainly got going,' he said. 'Bristling with heresies —but you certainly did get going.'

EIGHT

It was the last day of the voyage. Grimwade had gone to his cabin early to pack, as the boat would be berthing early in the morning. Burgeon and Chevalier, who had disposed of this chore earlier in the day, were alone together in a corner of the smoking-room.

'I suppose,' said the latter, 'we are not very likely to meet again.'

'I suppose not. I shall be the loser.' And after a brief pause, Burgeon was moved to add: 'There's one thing I'd rather like to ask you before we go our separate ways.'

'What is it?'

'Well, more than one thing really, I suppose. You remember roughly what we had been saying before I "got going", as you put it, the night before last? First of all, do you agree on the main issue—the one on which Grimwade and I *were* agreed? At one stage I put it in a kind of shorthand: Interior is anterior. Do you remember?'

'Of course I do. And as to agreeing, I couldn't do otherwise. Our minds are rational and logical by virtue of their participating in the divine Mind.'

'And would you say that the process of history is relevant in any way to that participation?'

'I would have thought not, since I don't hold—as obviously Grimwade and you don't either—that mind was a late-comer in history.'

'Thank you very much!' said Burgeon.

'Don't mention it,' said Chevalier, smiling. The smile was a delicate comment on the unaccountable eagerness with which Burgeon had spoken, rather like a child who had just been given a sweet. He was aware of it himself, but could not be bothered to check the tendency, and he continued with hardly less eagerness:

'But surely our *individual* minds *are* late-comers! I want to go back to the point where I "got going".'

'All that about paradise?'

'Yes. Must there not have been a different kind of participation in the time before the event recorded in the first chapter of Genesis?'

'I really don't know. Yes, I suppose so.'

'Surely it must have been very different!'

'It must. But not necessarily in the way you suppose.'

'Let us leave out what I suppose. I want to know what *you* suppose was the difference between before and after the Fall.'

'There is the difference between innocence and sin,' said Chevalier. 'Isn't that enough?'

'Not quite, I would have thought. For I take it you agree that the change was not simply a change in a subjective relation between man and God. It altered the whole face of creation, and in particular the human body.'

'I suppose I must admit that. From my recollection of the sort of thing you were saying, when you got going, I imagine you are now going to try and get me to agree that the Fall was a fall from spirit into matter. I warn you, you won't succeed.'

It was Burgeon's turn to smile. 'Very well,' he said. 'I won't try. But I think it is up to you to give me some idea of *how* the face of creation, or the world of nature, was changed by the Fall.'

'Is it? I am not nearly so anxious as you are to *know* about these mysteries. And I am not at all sure we are meant to. In any case, I wouldn't think it important in the way I see you do.'

'I am quite certain,' said Burgeon, 'that few things are more important. I have only to open a book or a newspaper to be appalled by the prospect of where our total ignorance of man's true origin is leading us. But I don't want to go on if you'd rather not.' Something in the earnestness with which he spoke must have touched Chevalier for there was a note of both kindness and respect in the voice with which he replied:

'I was always taught that the wages of sin is death. Perhaps that is the difference we are looking for.'

'Good,' said Burgeon, with the same curious intensity in his voice, curious to himself as well as to Chevalier. 'Hang on to that!' He paused and leaned back. 'Let us try to find a word,' he went on thoughtfully. 'We might get round the difficulty. You want to have it that there was matter before as well as after the Fall. But you agree—am I right?—that the former kind of matter was one that did not involve *death*. In that case I don't quite know how it differs from what *I* call "spirit"—but forget that—it's controversial. What we want is a word that's not controversial. Rather as they once made the word *gas* out of *chaos*; so that you could go on talking about "gas" without implying any judgments about "chaos" in any of its other meanings. You had a *neutral* word.'

'What do you suggest?'

'*Paradisal Matter*,' said Burgeon. 'Don't like it. Hm! How would the Germans do it? *Stoff*—*Para*—what else have we got? *Eden*. Shall we call it *Edenstuff*?'

'What a beastly word!'

'Yes. I suppose we shall have to use two words, after all. Would you agree to *Archetypal Matter*?'

'Well, go on anyway!'

'Very well. The transformation of the world of nature—including, of course, the human body—from a nature consisting of Archetypal Matter to a nature consisting of matter as we know it was an event occurring in history?'

'Only if you stretch the meaning of the word *history* out of all recognition.'

'Well, it was an event that occurred in time?'

'I'm not sure I can admit that either. Archetypal Matter may be timeless as well as deathless, for all I know.'

'But if so, you are saying that there was no time before the Fall! And *you* had the nerve to accuse *me* of heresy!'

'My dear fellow, we are just not permitted to *know* these things. You are still secretly trying to get me to agree that the Fall was a Fall into matter. I won't do it. Origenism involves Manicheism, and that—'

'Yes,' said Burgeon, 'I know you people raise the hue and cry of Manicheism at this point. The Fall was a fall into evil. If I say it was also a fall into matter, then I am saying that matter is evil. That is the argument, isn't it? But surely it is a fallacy. Suppose there is water in a cistern, you can't fall into the cistern without falling into the water; and because it is that particular bit of water you happen to be falling into, and no other, you can't fall into the water without falling into the cistern. Does it follow that the water is the cistern?'

'Very plausible—but your old trout is not to be caught with tickling.'

'Well, anyway, let us leave out Manicheism for the moment.

It was because I saw it coming that I suggested finding a neutral word. The point I wanted to make is that Christians, if they really are Christians, must reckon with a time before the Fall, just as they must reckon with a time before the Incarnation. They mostly fail, in my opinion, to do either. Yet surely the thing that more than all else distinguishes Christianity from other religions is that it does take *serious* account of time—and, unlike our friend Grimwade, not just short periods, not just the time of an individual biography. It accepts *historical* time as a reality, and a reality relevant to its own truth. Shall I go on?'

'Certainly,' said Chevalier. 'I hope nothing I said suggested that I am not interested. Whatever else I may accuse you of, it won't be of being a bore.'

Burgeon hesitated. 'You speak of accusing me,' he said, 'and, of course, you may accuse me of anything you like. Indeed, I sometimes wish these accusations were made more often and more openly. I mean that very seriously by the way, and I say it now because, if I do go on, I shall have some rather hard things to say to you.'

'Carry on,' said Chevalier imperturbably. And he got out his pipe and began filling it.

'Well then—when we were talking with Grimwade and he presented us with his Oriental dilemma, *either* the illusion of individual existence in time, *or* absorption in the timeless *One*—or something like that—you suggested that we had been saved from that dilemma by the Timeless choosing to enter into time.'

'I did.'

'And yet, when, a little later, he maintained that every generation is equidistant from eternity, you applauded. To be precise, you said: "Hear! hear!"'

'Is this one of the hard things you threatened me with?'

'No. But I haven't finished. If you rule out history as irrelevant to—what shall I say?—the main issue, the issue between the individual soul and what Grimwade would call eternity, or Brahma or Mind-Only or something, and you and I would call God—you blur the distinction between ourselves and Grimwade.'

'I hope not. But anyway it's not a very personal insult. I can take it.'

'But I still haven't finished! In doing that you unwittingly serve the purposes of—', Burgeon hesitated again—'Anti-Christ

92

is an emotive cry, almost a term of abuse—shall I call him the Adversary?'

'And in what way?'

'By denying that life on earth, as a whole, has any meaning.'

'I do not deny it at all. I say that the meaning, whatever it may be, is withheld from us.'

'But that is exactly what the agnostics said—and the beatniks imbibed from them with their mother's milk. And I don't mean by that a few young people in jeans and duffle-coats. I mean this whole beatnik generation.'

'You have left out one thing,' said Chevalier. 'The fact of revelation. The meaning of life on earth, so far as it is necessary for us to know it, was revealed to us by our Lord, both personally and through his Church. If we have a generation that refuses to accept it—', he shrugged his shoulders.

'Will you seriously maintain,' asked Burgeon, 'that future generations are ever going to return to accepting a revelation completed two thousand years ago as sufficient?'—a quick picture flitted through his mind of Willy sitting in a church listening to the Gospel and Epistle—'or even intelligible,' he added—'or that the practice of believing on authority will ever be generally resumed? In any case, your revelation has nothing to say *today*, as far as I can make out, on the two questions I have just raised—the time before the Fall, and the time before the Incarnation. Or the time after it, for that matter. How do they present the Incarnation to us? How does Charles Williams put it? "The flash and the prolongation." Isn't that about all the Romans can say of it, too?

'But people today are *interested* in history. And what have we to tell them in the light of that revelation? There was the flash two thousand years ago, and for the rest, for aeons before it and over the greater part of the earth after it—what? A haphazard agglomeration of events, with no detectable significance in it. History as H. A. L. Fisher sees it. History seen through the spectacles of natural science. You have left it to the Toynbees to try to do what *you* ought to have done. And when Chardin tries to make it good, according to his lights, which are not mine, from within the Church, he dare not even publish. He has to wait till he is dead.'

'I still wonder,' said Chevalier, 'if it is really as important as you suggest for people to find a meaning in history.'

'I will tell you one reason why it is important,' came the swift answer. 'As long as a man sees history as a meaningless jumble of events, he will see his own life—which is a part of history—and the lives of those around him in the same light. The other name for a meaningless jumble of events is one-damn-thing-after-another.'

'Well, it may be so. And it may be that people are more interested in history than they were. It is still only a very small fragment of the population that is affected, because it is only a very small fragment that is interested in ideas of any sort.' (Again the vision of Willy—but sharper and more urgent than before, so that Burgeon felt a flush of blood rising to his forehead. He dispersed the anger. After all, what had *he* ever done for Willy or his like, and what was he ever likely to do?)

'A small fragment that is directly affected,' he said, 'but that fragment includes the vocal ones. The ones who speak and are listened to. What sort of a picture are they presenting, not of history, but of *contemporary* life? Isn't it precisely—one-damn-thing-after-another, with no detectable thread between them? Look at a phenomenon like Surrealism; or look at what they call the New Drama. Moral indifferentism—*drift*, in fact—is not merely presented, it is presented as a kind of *summum bonum*, because it is based on what is believed to be the only certainly known truth about man. *Any* accepted system of values becomes automatically "the Establishment" and has to be rejected, not because there is anything wrong with it, but simply because it *is* a system. It is a pattern and therefore a lie, because the whole idea of a pattern in human events is rejected *in toto*. Take Pinter, for instance; incidents following each other without logic or motive, and facts contradicted as soon as they are established! Incidentally it makes for very bad plays; but that is not the point at the moment. The point is that the drama, good or bad, has always presented some kind of picture of the human being. And these plays are no exception. Only the picture *they* present is the picture of a rat in a trap, or a panic-stricken beetle hurrying aimlessly to and fro in search of a hole to hide in. You even get critics claiming that the picture is "intensely moral".'

'And are you suggesting that I am responsible for all this?'

'I am suggesting that the Church is in a large measure responsible.'

'I wonder,' said Chevalier, 'how much you really know about

the Catholic Church. I think it might surprise you how well aware they are of it, and how many devoted—and intelligent— people are striving to remedy it.'

'You misunderstand me. I am not suggesting that they are responsible because they wash their hands of it, or make no effort to cure it. I am suggesting that the Church is historically responsible for the disease.'

'If I have understood you at all,' said Chevalier, 'the root cause of the disease, as you see it, is the application of the principles of natural science to human history. Do you mean that the Church was responsible for the scientific revolution? I have never heard that one before. I have often heard her blamed for trying to *stop* the scientific revolution.'

Burgeon looked at him. 'We are coming to one of those hard things,' he said. 'I do not think the Church was responsible for the scientific revolution itself. That would have been a compliment. The trouble is that it was responsible for the particular path which science has since followed, and thus indirectly for those evil consequences of which we have just been speaking.'

'I think you will have to develop that a bit, you know.'

'What I have in mind,' said Burgeon, 'is the picture of man which has fastened down on the whole Western world: the picture of him as essentially a duality: first the duality of soul and body and then, since the scientific revolution, the same duality in its developed form of "the ghost in the machine", as it has been called. And now, as you know, the Adversary is busy disposing even of the remains of the ghost!'

'Yes. But *how* do you say the Church is responsible?'

'Because she deliberately set herself to ignore—or rather to obliterate—what we agreed just now to call Archetypal Matter —the unfallen spirit in man, which, as I would say, is not merely identical with his soul. That is why, in some ways, I feel more at home with Grimwade than I do with you.'

'Well, well!' said Chevalier. 'But how is all this relevant to the problem of history?'

'It is very relevant to the question with which we began: whether history can, or cannot, be understood as in any sense a process of evolution. And that,' added Burgeon with a sigh, 'brings us to the whole question of what anyone means by "evolution".'

It was his past traffic with the Meggid that had made him

sigh. He knew, or felt he knew, so clearly—and his tongue was so grievously tied! *Evolution is the process by which a past condition is transformed into a future one. Lucifer seeks to preserve the past from dissolution; Ahriman to destroy it utterly and substitute his own invention; Michael to transform it through death and rebirth.* To say that he knew by heart those farewell words from their last encounter is an understatement. They had long since become a part of him. Yet obviously he could not utter them, nor anything like them. What *could* he do? He could pull himself together. And even as he made the effort he recalled one of the Meggid's previous utterances, his insistence that the mere distinction between evolution and other kinds of change was a matter on which no help was needed. 'You can think it out for yourself,' he had said, and after all, Burgeon had done so. Could he reconstruct . . .? Chevalier's voice broke in on his reflections:

'You don't seem in a hurry to tackle the question!'

'It is a particular kind of change, isn't it?' Burgeon began. 'There are other kinds of change—one-damn-thing-after-another, for instance. I would call that kind mere substitution, whereas evolution implies a process of *transformation*. The difference between transformation and substitution is that transformation involves the persistent presence of something common to both the old form and the new. But where there is a total transformation of the material form, the something that persists must itself be immaterial.'

'Why?'

'Otherwise the transformation would not be total.'

'Yes. I see,' said Chevalier. 'That seems right.'

'Can I call this persistent, immaterial base the "transforming agent"?' Chevalier nodded. Burgeon was aware of a faint malaise in himself, a sort of spiritual perspiration. He would have been glad of the Meggid's help. It was not forthcoming. He suddenly decided to take a big leap forward.

'You agree, presumably,' he continued, 'that all things were made by the Divine Word, or Logos?' Again Chevalier nodded. 'You know, of course, that the word St. John actually uses there is *egeneto*—which would normally mean something more like "came into being", or "was born", or indeed simply "came to pass"?'

'You flatter me,' said Chevalier. 'I am not a Greek scholar.

Am I to understand that you are saying it is a false translation?'

'I do not say it is a wholly impossible one. It is merely unlikely to be quite adequate. I believe there are two passages in the whole of the New Testament where the word *egeneto* has been translated in that way, whereas it occurs all over the place in the other senses—one of them in the very passage we are speaking of.'

'I suspect you are trying to blur the all-important distinction, emphasized in the Creed, between *begetting* and *creating*.'

'Maybe,' said Burgeon briefly. 'Or maybe there are other things even more important.'

'I should doubt it very much.'

'Well, let us leave it for the moment. I take it—and this is one of the things I wanted to ask you—that you do not believe the world was created in the beginning by the Logos—wound up, and set going, like Paley's watch—and then left to look after itself?'

'I really do not claim to know.'

'Believe,' I said.

'I am not sure whether I—no, I suppose I don't.'

'Then, whether we call it making, or creating, or begetting, or coming into being, the activity of the Logos still persists today?'

'As I say, I really don't know. But I would think so, yes.'

'The ordinary theory of evolution does not agree with you.'

'That does not worry me much. As a matter of fact, I am not particularly *interested* in evolution.'

'No,' said Burgeon, 'I have discovered that. Nor is Grimwade. That is why I am not sure if you really want to go on.'

He had spoken so intensely that Chevalier, who took things easily, looked at him with a faintly comic air of exaggerated apprehensiveness, as he replied: 'Come on. Let us hear some more hard things.'

'When we happened to get talking of Dryden two or three days ago, and afterwards of the Court of Louis XIV,' said Burgeon slowly, 'we all three of us remarked how strangely eighteenth-century France and England were overshadowed by the ghost of Rome. Well, in my opinion we are where we are now, because much the same thing happened to the whole of Western culture at its birth. To say that it happened at the birth of Western culture is the same thing as saying that it happened within the Church, because the Church was the cradle of Western culture. But it is still going on. That is why we have a culture, a world of thought, which is wholly unchristian and, tucked away in a corner of it, a Christianity which is no Christianity. Don't misunderstand me. I am not raising the cry of "No-popery". I am not thinking of High Church or Low Church. When I say that Western Christianity is Roman through and through, I am thinking as much, or more, of the broad or liberal types, who are farthest from "Rome", than I am of the others. Oh no! We no longer acknowledge the supremacy of the Pope—any more than the eighteenth-century statesmen actually *wore* the Roman togas you see on their statues. But our Barneses and Robinsons are possessed by the ghost of Rome all the same in every innocent thought they think. Because they mainly think that they have somehow to reconcile Christianity with twentieth-century science, or rather, *not* with twentieth-century science, but with the whole blessed historical fantasy of nineteenth-century science—scientism—"Wellsianity", or whatever you like to call it. And the reason why we had Wellsianity was because the original bias of Western science was determined by the ghost of Rome. Perhaps it was necessary. Perhaps the Adversary himself is necessary. But that is not the point. The point is : what to do *now*.

'And what is "Rome"—Rome in inverted commas—doing ? Straining every nerve to keep the ghost alive, even in its external, religious forms, as the eighteenth century did in its little way with the external and aesthetic forms. Making a fetish of the ghost itself—the ghost that is responsible for the "two cultures" we heard so much of a little while ago, the ghost that is responsible for the philosophy of "life equals one-damn-thing-after-another", that is responsible for the revival in the last hundred years of an Orientalism that really belongs to the past, since those who think deeply and take the spirit seriously will inevitably turn to where the spirit is at least *recognized*.'

'You are going rather too fast for me,' said Chevalier. 'Perhaps taking me out of my depth. I thought just now you were going to say that the Church ought to have produced its own doctrine of evolution, as a sort of counter-blast to Darwin—'

'It comes to that. Let us go back to where we were. You said you were not specially interested in evolution and you didn't mind a bit if the ordinary theory of evolution does not agree with you. Right?'

'I did.'

'But *why* doesn't it agree?'

'I thought *you* were going to tell *me* that.'

'I am. Either all things were made, and are sustained, by the Logos, or they were not. If they were, then the Logos is, in some way, the transforming agent underlying the changes in both nature and history. The ordinary theory of evolution is what it is because by the time men first became aware of evolution they no longer knew anything of that transforming agent. And it is that very ignorance for which Rome is responsible at the bar of history.'

'You say so—but why?'

'Because Rome would have nothing to do with . . . Archetypal Matter.'

'This is a very odd conversation,' said Chevalier. 'Now, I remember you did say something a little while back about Archetypal Matter still present in the soul, only this time you also called it "unfallen spirit": I let it pass, but it didn't seem to follow from anything we had actually said.'

'Perhaps not. But why did we have to bring in Archetypal Matter at all? You had agreed that our minds are rational by virtue of participating in the Divine Mind, that is (or rather, whence proceeds) the Logos, by whom all things were made, and you further agreed that that participation was more intimate before the Fall. But you did not want to agree that the Fall was a fall into "matter". If you agree, as I think you do, that we *still* participate in some measure and that we once participated more fully and intimately, then we don't really need any such outlandish term. We can use the word "spirit".'

'Very well. I certainly agreed that we are rational by virtue of our participation in the Divine Mind. But you seem to be suggesting something more.'

'Because there was a time when it *was* something more. It is really obvious, you know—if only from the history of language —that human beings were at one time directly aware of having within their minds the Spirit which created them and created the rest of the world, too.'

'That sounds to me suspiciously like Grimwadism—of which, incidentally, *you* have twice accused *me*!'

'No. Grimwade is not interested in participating; he is only interested in disappearing. That is the whole difference between East and West. It is the whole difference between Orientalism and Christianity. Let me try to go on. If I am right, the transition from East to West—the transition of the centre of gravity of civilization from East to West—signified the change that was taking place in human consciousness *from* awareness of a sort of *residual* participation in the Divine Mind, or creative Spirit, *to* an awareness only of *exclusion* from that participation. *But*—and this is really not difficult to see (it only needs a smattering of psychology)—it is that very exclusion which gives to a man his separate, independent existence. It is this that bestows its inviolate *integrity* on his personality, for good or ill. What was Kierkegaard's phrase?—"Directness is paganism." Residual participation is at best instinctual—sibylline—mediumistic. But once a human self has been emancipated from instinct to the extent of being fully aware of its own existence—if it *then* seeks to resume its unity with the Divine Mind, it first has to die. There is clearly no other way. Grimwade's people know this and they know it better than we do. That is their strength. But, for them, the dying of the soul means simply its becoming unborn again. They understand unborn-ness, but not immortality. Immortality implies transformation. That is why they are not interested in transformation—or in evolution, which is its other name. Every transformation is a process of death and rebirth. I do not see how we can understand Christianity otherwise than as the opportunity given to human souls to unite themselves with the Spirit; and *not* with a Spirit which takes care not to be born, but with a Spirit that dies *and is reborn*. What else but that does St. Paul really insist on? And how much of a Church would there be if there had been no St. Paul? Am I boring you?'

Chevalier shook his head.

'Well, where have we got to? We were talking about history and evolution. Surely, if there is anything in what I have been saying, it is pretty relevant to the proper understanding of both! And it is just that understanding which I accuse the Church of strangling at its birth. In doing so, it has severed the past from the future, so that we have no understanding of evolution; and it has severed the East from the West, so that we have no understanding of history.'

'I still do not understand why you blame the Church.'

'Past and future are *united* only by a self-same Spirit that sustains the death and rebirth which all transition involves. Any other spirit can only substitute one form or event for another. Indeed, it is only by living in that Spirit that we can ever really live in the present at all. Outside it, we merely chronicle the past and shun or grab at the future. That is why Christians contemplate with reverence and love—the corpse which Buddha could only abhor! And, in my view, without some understanding of history as evolution we cannot be living in that Spirit.'

'Are you seriously saying a man cannot be a good Christian unless he is a sound historian?'

'If the mental plane he lives on is such that he gives any attention to history—yes.'

'You *still* have not explained how the Church is responsible.'

'Because it eliminated the Spirit.'

'Eliminated?'

'Eliminated the whole concept of Spirit—though she still used the *word*. Removed it from the category of things needing to be understood, from the category of things that are knowable, or even thinkable. But she went farther than that. She denied the very presence of the Spirit in the human soul. By doing so, she left the West with that forlorn duality of soul and body, of ghost and machine, which has ever since determined the shape of its science, its history and its so-called doctrine of evolution.

'It was not always so. The immemorial wisdom of the East concerning the Spirit was not always repudiated by the West, because it was not always repudiated by the Church. But it was in the Church that the rift between East and West began. You have referred to Origenism. I was surprised that you did not also bring in Gnosticism. It is customary, whenever orthodoxy sniffs the breath of that wisdom. And yet it goes so much deeper than that. I am not thinking of the rejection of particular doctrines. It was the anathematizing of the Spirit itself that was the disaster, for it was this that severed humanity from its own past, and in doing so, murdered history.'

For some time now Burgeon had been aware that the Meggid was, in effect, once more speaking in him. He was the less surprised to hear his own voice propounding things that he did not even know that he knew. 'Go back a thousand years and more,' that voice continued. 'Go back to the time of the Photian schism.

The quarrel, historians tell us, between Photius and Pope Nicholas the First began about Bulgaria—but—'

'I am not well up in Church history,' said Chevalier. 'But I always thought it was about the *Filioque* in the Creed.'

'You are wrong, and we need not waste time on it. Because you can easily convince yourself. The quarrel, they tell us, and no doubt rightly, began about the Bulgarian Christians. But the historians throw little enough light on the mysterious figure of Photius himself nor succeed in explaining how it came about that, to this day, the man who is revered as a saint by the Eastern Church is represented in the West as a sort of prince of gerrymanderers. Is it surprising that they have little, or nothing, to say, either, of the most momentous event of all? They faithfully record the Council of Constantinople—the Eighth Oecumenical Council of 869, which the Eastern Church has always refused to recognize—and yet they have nothing to say of its tenth Canon.'

'Why, what is in the tenth Canon?'

'It anathematizes all who believe that the spirit is present in the human soul. It does not use precisely those terms. The draughtsman first distorts—perhaps deliberately, perhaps through misunderstanding—what he then proceeds to condemn; reciting the existence of a heretical belief that man has two souls. But it is a strange heresy which has, as far as I know, no history and no heresiarch; and the true significance of the Canon is clear enough, at least if you know anything of the previous history of dogma. The real point at issue was the Dionysian teaching of the Divine Hierarchies—whether it should continue to be studied and meditated, or should be lost sight of for four or five centuries.

'The real purpose of the Roman party was not to condemn a supposititious fantasy of two distinct human souls; it was to debar everyman's one awakening soul from its heritage or participation in the Spirit. Why? Because the Roman party could only conceive of the soul as the ghost of a Roman citizen owing allegiance to the ghost of a Roman Caesar.

'Henceforth the Church was to see her children not as eternal spirits but as timeous souls. Therefore she had to abolish the Spirit altogether, except as a name and an abstraction—and therefore she gradually scribbled over the sublime image of God the Father all those insipidities of God the Paterfamilias. The Protestants did indeed dethrone the *visible* phantom of the

Roman Caesar—the earthly one in the Vatican—but they only domesticated the heavenly Paterfamilias more than ever. God the Paterfamilias was turned by them into God the papa; and as to the soul—as to the poor human soul—the ghost of the Roman citizen has lived on to become the ghost in the machine!'

'Still at it?' said Grimwade's voice, as he came up behind their armchairs. 'Haven't you settled the hash of history yet?'

'No,' replied Chevalier, 'but I have learned one thing, while you have been packing, and that is that our friend Burgeon has got hold of a really interesting heresy, and I should say a deep-rooted one. Or perhaps it has got hold of him.' He paused and seemed to be reassembling his forces. 'What I am asking myself, in my quiet way,' he went on, 'is: how long it will last? Perhaps history *can* give us a line on that. He has just taken me back a thousand years. I will give him another thousand. What will have happened to your heresy by then? What has happened to all the others?'

Suddenly diffident, and depressed by the almost fraudulent contrast between himself and the Meggid, who had just left him, Burgeon answered slowly, looking at the ground as he spoke: 'I don't know. But I rather think things have begun to move faster than that. Perhaps it is its fate in the next *hundred years* that we should really be thinking of.'

NINE

The boat that had allowed the minds of those three travellers to meet docked very early on its arrival. Their destinations were different, and before six o'clock they had parted in the hurry of the customs shed with mutual expressions of goodwill. Burgeon never met either of the other two again.

Their conversation had finished very late, and Burgeon, with his packing still to do and his brain too active, had hardly slept at all during his last night on board. Awakening next morning in his hotel bedroom, he realized that he had been making up for the lack. He felt the long dreamless night behind him, at first, as an enormous heaviness in his limbs which he should never shake off. And then, as that heaviness began to detach itself slightly, so that it was now something he could contemplate, instead of simply *being* it, he slowly came to realize, as he had never quite succeeded in doing before, the identity between precisely this heaviness and the recreation which was sleep. The hugeness of the one was the hugeness of the other caught, as it were, in the act; so that during the day that was coming the intolerable might of its oppressive mass would be the effortless ease with which his will would again inform those inert limbs, or with which (as long as they were passive) his mind would exploit their passivity for its own vigilance. There was, after all, no more mysterious transformation than this nightly one of the fagged and jaded into the active and energetic. How could one ever hope to understand the transformation of matter into energy, of the heaviness of matter into the weightlessness of energy, without seeking also to penetrate this? For this *was* the transformation of matter into energy; only it was the inside of it.

And now he knew that the Meggid was coming to him, with power; and with tidings. This time, he felt, it would not be for him to put questions, but only to receive. And yet there *was* a question which he had wanted to ask. Half asleep as he still was, he struggled feebly to concentrate, to recall it—almost, one could say, to 'get in first'. Why, he enquired, why, when the three of us were talking together, and reincarnation was mentioned—it was just before you began to speak yourself—why did you lay your finger on my lips?

The Meggid spoke:

It would have spoiled, by confusing it, what was then going forward. You were not fully aware of it—and if you had been, you might well have become tiresomely didactic—but you had set yourself a definite task. It was to establish, if possible, first that there is indeed an 'interior transforming agent', secondly that man has direct access to it, and thirdly—after Grimwade had left you—that that is your name for the Logos, the Word which became flesh.

A year ago you were asking yourself in what manner human consciousness can be said to be not merely the result, but a transformation, of the remote past into which the biologists peer. They speak of 'emergent' evolution; yet it is not emergence which they describe but the results of innumerable substitutions begun by chance. You saw that the real problem was the emergence, or evolution, of individual human minds from their natural and spiritual background. You fixed your attention, as always, on the evolution of consciousness and you rightly found a partial answer in the nature of the human word, in the origin and history of speech. But that alone is not a sufficient answer. It is only through repeated earth-lives that mind could *gradually*, and as an historical process, become more and more individualized, that is to say, could gradually emerge from the spirit which gave birth to it and from the nature which it is learning to contemplate from without instead of merely participating from within. From that contemplation it derives its separate existence, from that participation its *continuous* existence; and therefore the condition of its being is that these two states shall rhythmically alternate.

Does it not follow that, as the transformation—as the 'awakening', of which you were endeavouring to speak to your friends, proceeds, the light in which men behold the truth of repeated lives is itself transformed? The sleep into which a man is still struggling—as you were struggling a few minutes ago—to *get* back is the same and yet it is not the same as the sleep to which he *looks* back, after he has woken. So then the concept of repeated earth-lives has itself been transformed, has itself evolved, and the occidental understanding of it, which is only today beginning to awaken, bears little relation to the Oriental perspective which Grimwade, for instance, accepts, and Chevalier, for instance, abhors and repudiates. Therefore, to have become involved with them in a discussion concerning 'reincarnation' could only have darkened counsel, confusing the issue which you were just beginning to make clear.

Yet *you* should now be prompt to understand it well. I am to remain with you longer on this occasion. Let us begin by retracing our steps in reverse order through some of the thoughts you have partly derived from me and partly achieved by your own effort. Evolution is transformation. Complete transformation entails the persistence of an immaterial transforming agent. But your awareness of that agent is, so far as possible, persistently obliterated by Lucifer and Ahriman. Now, in the case of biological evolution there is a clear enough distinction between the actual process of transformation and anyone's knowledge of that process. But in the case of the evolution of consciousness itself, that distinction progressively fades. Recall now what I once said to you of the dawn of the Michael age, and of that recent and still proceeding emergence from a quasi-instinctual life of the mind into a vigilant one. It was, I remind you, at the same time an emergence from group unity into individual unities. But that is only true of man's waking life. He still sleeps from time to time and, while he sleeps, is no longer an isolated unit. In sleep his consciousness subsides into the instinctual life which sustains him—subsides there so completely indeed that it is almost wholly submerged and overwhelmed. So it is now; it will not always be so. There should be no danger of your taking the word 'instinctual' here in the sense in which biology speaks of 'instinct' nor even with the crass, though deeper, overtones which it bore for such a mind as Lawrence's. They were no merely physical energies that still helped to sustain the men of the preceding age. They were beings. I spoke then only of the being whom we called Gabriel, but behind him, active in him and one with him, are ranged all the hierarchies of his fellow beings in the spiritual world. And so it still is for sleeping, though not for waking, humanity.

It is only in this light that anyone can today understand the truth of repeated earth-lives. His rhythmic alternation between contemplation and participation is infinitely varied for the race of man. The phase of its beat is now short, now long, and now again very long. It is latent in his breathing and even in the pulsation of his heart and blood. It is most clearly manifest in the succession of nights and days, of which the biography of even the alertest mind consists. But as waking is followed by sleeping, and that again by waking, so is life followed by death and that again by life. In the time which is coming those who are concerned to trace the course of history and of the evolution of consciousness will learn to investigate not only the contemplative and waking one of the two poles, between which that evolution swings, but also the participating and sleeping one. And they will learn—as the Oriental grasp of reincarnation could not possibly learn—to follow its course in both phases, not only the forward flow between birth and death, but also the backward ebb between death and birth. They will come to feel that the one half of the picture they try to form of it is almost meaningless without the other.

Some day it may be that *you* will learn more of this from *me*—will learn, even into detail, how the lower part of the physical organism, or let us say the part through which will and desire have functioned on earth, the part which remains instinctual and asleep even when the head is awake—how all this is transformed between one life and the next, disappearing into the bosom of the hierarchies for some hundreds of years and then reappearing on earth as the head and the brain of the new organism. But not now.

Reflect that it is meaningless to speak, historically, of the gradual emergence of individual consciousness from any other form of consciousness, unless the individual unit, once it has been recognizably attained, persists. For once that stage has been reached it may be fittingly compared with any other persistent form, such as a biological species. The death of one body, followed, without more, by the birth of another, would be substitution, not transformation—unless some transforming agent persisted. In the evolution of humanity the transforming agent is the spirit—and, as time proceeds, it is more and more the individual spirit. This is the only 'emergence' which is not a mere trifling with words.

I have tried to show you how that emergence is rhythmically accomplished, as is the incoming of a tide with its advancing, and yet continually withdrawing, waves. While he is dead—and then also during his life, while he is asleep—the slowly and painfully emerging individual spirit is again encapsuled for a time within the choir of the hierarchies who brought about its birth and who foster its growth to maturity; yet—more within them now, as more without them when he was awake in his earthly life—he himself becomes increasingly the co-agent of his own transformation. It was the knowledge, it was the very possibility of conceiving this contained identity of the individual spirit within the whole world of the spirit, which, as you rightly pointed out to your friends, was suppressed by the Western Church. But first I wished you to be clear, from what I have said, that the Western understanding of man's repeated earth-lives, when at last it does awaken, will be very different from, indeed, it will be virtually opposite to, the Oriental doctrine of 'reincarnation'. For it will not, as the East has done, lay the whole emphasis on the period of life on earth, but will well understand that the opposite pole, the period purgatorial and celestial between death and birth, is of at least equal significance for the present predicament of the human soul; and it will seek to investigate that, too . . . as you are doing at this moment. And secondly it will, though with a sober realization of the cost in suffering, see rebirth as a thing to be sought rather than one to be avoided.

But this can come about only as the crude duality of soul and body, or mind and body, comes to be superseded by a growing understanding of threefold human nature in body, soul and spirit. Do not underestimate the strength of the great barrier which stands in the way of this understanding. In one form or another, soul and body, ghost and machine, flitting idea and solid flesh, the duality is now an *idée fixe*. It is true that the *word* 'spirit' is used often enough—but, outside the Churches, only as a synonym for soul or mind, only as a name for what is still thought of as contained within the body; and, within the Churches, only as a technical term to which no understanding is brought. The tabu bars all approach to an awareness of the encompassing spirit that persists and sustains through the transformation that is waking and sleeping and through the transformation that is life and death; it persuades the mind that the borderland between the non-spatial and the spatial manifestations of spirit cannot and should not be broached by the understanding. Its foundation was deliberately laid, as you have seen, at a time when the form of

Western thought was itself yet young and delicate. And as the twig was bent, the tree has grown. In the course of the centuries, as the forms of Western thought have strengthened and hardened, the barrier has been entrenched and fortified by the two adversaries, till today it has become a tabu. Even to think of crossing it is indecent. It takes courage to disregard a tabu. Among your contemporaries, every time some merely sexual or social tabu is deliberately flouted, let us say by a writer, he is praised by a few for his courage. But such tabus are as nothing to the one I am speaking of. Perhaps it may call for some little courage to disregard a tabu that is already weakening here and there, so that the innovator knows he will win acclaim as well as disapproval. If so, that is still nothing compared with the courage it demands to flout a tabu that is still universal and unshaken. The one I am speaking of is of this kind. The scientist bows before it, because the whole of his science is founded on it; the philosopher because he has taken his cue from science and would now rather eliminate the ghost than sacrifice the machine; the religious because, for him, God must be God the Paterfamilias or nothing; the artist—nowhere perhaps than here has the strength of the tabu shown itself more plainly. For the soul of the artist is a questioning soul, and it has been sorely tempted. No longer content to represent the face of the earth *on* which, and the earthly life *in* which, it finds itself, the mind of the artist longs obscurely for the true way out of its *impasse*, longs to escape from the slavery of imitation by penetrating to the creative source from which life springs, and to create afresh from there. Yet, rather than infringe the tabu, it has sought to escape by expressing any imbecile whim and inventing any insipid abstraction, which will avoid the charge of 'naturalness'.

And yet perhaps I have spoken too hastily; perhaps there is one type of mind even more firmly in the grip of this tabu than any of these I have yet spoken of. I mean the revolutionary, the soul that prides itself precisely on its determination to flout or smash *all* established tabus. For in his case the *paramount* tabu lurks in still more secret depths and is tangled at its very roots with the angry bias of his energy. To become aware of this— even to fancy such a thing possible—would require what he most lacks, humility; worse, it would lead to an understanding of the meaning of the past and its persistence and value in the present. You know why he will have none of this.

The Meggid paused.

All this, said Burgeon, I have heard and partly understood. Yet there is one thing of which I would learn more from you, if it is allowed, before you leave me again. I have thought, and I have seemed to understand from you—at least implicitly—that there is an essential relation between all you have told me, both now and previously, and the birth, life and death of the one man, Jesus of Nazareth. Yet you have said little of it. Will you now say more?

The silence of the Meggid suggested that he was waiting for the questioner himself to say more.

When the three of us were talking on the ship, Burgeon continued at last, one of my two friends spoke of those events as the entry of the Timeless into time. That—how am I to put it other than lamely?—that sounded right, and I accepted it. Was I right or wrong? How am I to think of that historical event, and of that man? You have spoken much to me of evolution, of a gradual emergence of the individual spirit of man from the Father Spirit that created it; you have spoken, too, of a long series of deaths and rebirths as the necessary rhythmical process of that emergence. If I am right about the essential relation, and if my friend was not wholly wrong when he spoke of the Timeless entering into time, what have you to say of that particular birth and of that particular death? Were they also only one of many suffered, and to be suffered, by the same individuality? How can that be so? And yet how can it not be so?

We have recorded on one previous occasion that the Meggid, or so it seemed to his questioner, 'sighed' before bringing himself to answer. This time it would perhaps be more faithful to the impression Burgeon received to say that he groaned. At last, however, he gave utterance.

I have been speaking to you, he said, perhaps too severely, of a tabu. But I have not spoken too emphatically. I have not exaggerated its strength. Rather if anything I have understated it. And it is nowhere more violent than here. But here, if anywhere, it has also some justification. For these are very holy mysteries which I, even I, feel some horror of seeking to clothe in words, or rather in your thoughts that lean so heavily on words. Yet I know that I must overcome it. For I know that I am the servant of Michael—and do I not daily behold the encroachments of the adversaries and see increasing upon earth

110

an ominous chaos which knowledge, and knowledge alone, can order? No matter where the seed falls, in how remote a corner of humanity; it falls here; it falls there; because it is a seed it will grow from where it fell. Take, then, a seed of knowledge. Receive it without prejudice, as always, but not without solemnity, not without the deepest breath of responsibility yon are able to draw from the inmost recesses of your being, from all you have ever reverenced, all you have ever suffered, all you have ever witnessed or tremulously imagined of suffering in others, since your life began.

You have spoken—rightly, in your contexts—of a transforming agent; and we have together placed side by side and distinguished the agent from man's knowledge of the agent; and we have seen how these are none the less drawing closer together. But *I* must now speak, using other names, of the Christ and of Michael his Countenance. Rather, I have already spoken somewhat of his Countenance and I must now speak of the Christ himself.

The persistence and the operation of the transforming agent, through the death of the old into the life of the new form, are mysterious enough in the case of the commonest weed that dies in the autumn and remains dead until its timeless form is born again in the spring. What, then, would you have in the case of the transforming agent of the earth-planet itself with the race of mankind and all else that lives upon it? You are learning, you men, that the workings of the spirit, when it enters into space, are complex enough; yet many of you like to think that up to the point of entry it was all a childish simplicity. No. Transformation, even the humblest, is effected by no instantaneous trick and it would be strange if the archetype of all transformations had been the only exception.

What is transformation? You have asked the question before. Ask it now again. If there is continuity, it is not transformation, you say; yet if there is no continuity, then, too, it is not transformation; for then there is only substitution. There must then be a total discontinuity and yet it must be overcome. *We* here have no acquaintance with total discontinuity. We only know it is called 'death'. It was for man on his earth to introduce that into the community of spirits, as it is now for man on his earth to overcome it—for himself and us. But how?

The fruit of many earth-lives, the germ of unfallen spirit in the soul of man—original—paradisal—exempt from death—and the

Timeless entering into time to re-create the new from the old, redeeming death into life—all these things should be in your mind, and all these things would needs be understood more deeply and in detail, before the great Transformation that underlies all earthly transformation is understood and followed—as it must soon be followed—in the questioning mind of man. I need not speak again of the barrier. And yet—have I even now impressed it enough on you? You may believe, if you think fit—for it is true—that there are those who would rather see the earth itself destroyed—as indeed it may yet be destroyed—than that the seal should be broken which has so long been laid upon the truth I am now to utter.

Because you are as yet totally ignorant of it, I shall for your sake approach it, not from our archetypal light, in which it shines clear and obvious, but from the opposite direction of your darkness—even the darkness of those few vestiges to be traced in the surviving records. Fix now your mind upon those records, upon that testament. Apart from three names, which are the same in both narratives, if it were possible for you to read, with a mind empty of all tradition and therefore of all 'prejudice', the opening chapters first of the Gospel of St. Matthew and then of the Gospel of St. Luke, you would find in them records of the births and infancies of two children; one of whom was born in Bethlehem, where his parents resided; whose cradle was visited by three Eastern sages; whose parents took him with them to Egypt and, when they returned, returned not to Bethlehem but to Nazareth, in order to be out of Herod's jurisdiction. The other child, so you would read, was born of a mother who resided, not in Bethlehem, but in Nazareth. Her labour began while she was passing through Bethlehem on her way to Jerusalem and she gave birth to the child, not in her own home but in the stable of an inn, where his hastily contrived cradle was visited by a group of shepherds. His parents did not turn aside to Egypt, but continued their journey to Jerusalem, where the child was circumcised a week later and, a little later still, was presented in the temple. It would perhaps surprise you, but not greatly—for they were three of the commonest names in that time and place—if you afterwards learned that the names, both of the two couples and of the two infants, were the same. It would surprise you, but not enough to make you conclude that the two narratives refer to the same child. And in this you would be right, for they were, in fact, two children and not one. The soul of Jesus of Bethlehem was indeed the fruit of many previous lives, and there is allusion to this in the genealogy which precedes the account of his birth, and which is traced back only to Abraham—that is, approximately to the stage of emergence of which I spoke—when individuality had for the first time been recognizably attained by the human spirit. All Jews were the children of Abraham and both these children were also of the royal line of David. Jesus of Bethlehem, however, traced his descent through David's royal son King Solomon, and his ancestors thereafter were, according to your record, different from the ancestors of Jesus of Nazareth. The physical pedigree of Jesus of Nazareth is drawn from David through another son, the priest Nathan. But the provenance of the *soul* that was born in this Jesus is a deeper mystery. It had known no previous lives on earth. It was indeed an Eden-soul, unfallen, and given intact from the Father Spirit to be the persisting link between the old state of the human spirit and the new. Again there is a gentle allusion, for the genealogy is here traced back beyond Abraham, to Adam, who, says the record, 'was the son of God'; allusion also in the paradisal aura, the breath of pastoral innocence, which pervades this second narrative, as you know so well.

And now believe—if you think fit—that the fruit of his previous lives, that the very personality of the first child was offered up by him to the second. Again you will find a vestige of that ineffable sacrifice in the Gospel of St. Luke. You will find it in the astonishment that befell the parents of Jesus of Nazareth at the sudden change that took place in him during their visit to Jerusalem in his twelfth year. The two children had become one. I am not speaking physically. Do not ask me. If you have the will, you will find where the physical consequences are described. Think only of those two souls—through what millennia prepared for that moment!—uniting to form, as it were, a chalice in which the Timeless, in which the Timeless that both dies and dies not, could indeed enter into time—as it did when the man Jesus was baptized by John in the River Jordan, and the uncreated light, the untransformed transforming, entered his consciousness and became also the Christ of history.

I need not tell you, for you have heard and read many times, how, immediately thereafter, he encountered first Lucifer and then Ahriman in the great solitude. And this he did on behalf of all mankind—if they will have it so. They cannot by his deed escape their own encounter, yet they can be certain of victory if they unite themselves with him, so that it is not they, but he within them, who confronts those adversaries. But, for this grace *today*, they need knowledge as well as virtue—the knowledge that he, whom they are finding, and will not recognize, as the transforming agent in nature, is also the ultimate energy that stirs in the dark depths of their own wills; and that all else that stirs there is the work of the one adversary or the other.

This, then, said Burgeon, is the *energeia* of which St. Paul so raptly speaks?

It is indeed.

And how if it be still *not* recognized?

It has its own laws, which it does not cease to obey because they are misused. Every child who plays with fire, or with his own body, learns this. And I and my fellows know it in sorrow when, because we cannot *not* act, we needs must act destructively. That which is the might of the spirit within you, when it is encountered from without, as it must be if you are to be freed from its compulsion, is—nature. Will you choose to confront her, then, as enemy whom you vainly hope to capture and enslave, or will you seek to welcome and understand her as friend? Recall your own struggle with sleep this morning. The friend who is now within you ready to move the weight of your body where you will, so that you cease to be even aware of it— did it not press upon you as a huge enemy, so that it seemed to *be* that weight . . . until it entered within you and revealed itself as the refreshment of sleep? I am helping you to penetrate the great illusion, which is one with the great tabu. And this is the illusion. The relation between yourself and nature is, not a rela- tion between your body and all else in nature, but the relation between yourself on the one hand and, on the other, your body as at once a part of nature and her epitome.

It is true, said Burgeon, and how few, how very few, as yet will admit to their minds even the fancy that it *might* be true! Lawrence, with his ignorance and his inkling, was at least one of that few.

I know, said the Meggid, what is coming into your mind and am glad of it. The chaos of which I spoke just now is not *only* the chaos which the rapid advance of your technology is threatening. You yourself have encountered it more intimately elsewhere—

in the social relations between man and man, between old and young, between man and woman, between society itself and its criminals. But the relevance of all *this* to the Christ of recorded history is not undiscovered. It is indeed often proclaimed; yet it will not long continue to be proclaimed, unless they learn whom in truth it is that they are proclaiming—by finding him present otherwise, too, than in the gospels and in the eucharist and in their own subjectivity. The subjective need will soon by any reckoning be desperate enough; but not therefore, not therefore do I come to *you*. I point you not to social chaos—it is evident enough and will soon be more so—but to the source of that chaos; and, if you choose to follow where I point, you will now for a time seek him rather in the world of nature than in the world of man. Listen in that regard—and listen from those same responsible depths to which I just now appealed—to one further thing I will say before I leave you.

It breaks ground that is new between us, for I come now to speak of *science*—and not this time as a portion of history, but as the growing-point of man's present mental activity.

There are two aims which research may innocently pursue. It may seek for knowledge of nature, and it may seek, even in awareness of its ignorance, to evoke and control her powers. In your science the first aim was commoner in the past; the second developed with the discovery of electricity and has grown rapidly with the advance of sub-atomic and nuclear research. But when, as now, the two aims are identified, when the search for knowledge, as men once understood the word, is abandoned, and it begins to be maintained (as it is often now maintained) that that control *is* knowledge, and is moreover the only knowledge available to the race of man, then research is no longer innocent. For ask yourself what it signifies. To know anything—whether a person, a thing or a process—entails, as you have already found with me, that the mind enters into what is known and unites with the spirit that informs and transforms it. It is, in greater measure or less, a process of the Logos itself. But what process are we to call it, when this is no longer even attempted—perhaps emphatically repudiated? What hostages do you suppose, in the light of all I have told you, mankind is offering to his determined adversaries, when you see his mind, which is at home beyond the confines of earth, reduced to 'monkeying' from without with the earth-body it should be striving to inform from within?

What you have described, said Burgeon slowly, is a kind of cosmic masturbation.

Think farther of it, said the Meggid earnestly. Think farther of this, when you are reflecting, as you will, on other things that I have brought myself to tell you today, Pursue it! And now farewell.

PART THREE

TEN

The lecturer was a young man under thirty. A rather brilliant piece of research had recently won him the respect of the Physical Society, whose members, together with a few invited guests, he was now addressing. Before that and before specializing, he had received his scientific education at one of the increasing number of new universities where the winds of apprehension concerning the 'two cultures' had just begun to blow; with the result that he had learned something, if not very much, of the general history of natural science and the scientific approach; and some attempt had been made to help him, before his immersion in it, to see from outside the place occupied by his own narrow activity in the whole field of human endeavour. Later he had had the advantage or, as some of his colleagues thought, the disadvantage of working for a time under Professor David Bohm. He had chosen as the title of his address *The Crisis in Microscopic Physics*.

He began his paper with an apology. It would be impossible to avoid starting with a brief historical résumé, and that, he knew, would involve his wasting the time of most of his audience by going through stuff with which they were already tiresomely familiar. Perhaps it would be useful to one or two among their visitors.

He did not think that the topic on which he was privileged to address them—and it would be part of his task to justify his use of the word 'crisis'—could be considered without casting one's mind for a moment a little way back in the history of physics. A very little way. Indeed, it was surprising to reflect how short a time had elapsed since the break with classical physics—by which one meant, roughly, Newton's laws for the motion of massive bodies and Clark Maxwell's describing the behaviour of electromagnetic radiation—and the transition to modern microscopic and sub-microscopic physics. Let him briefly recall some of the teething troubles of this comparatively young child of the human brain—which was, after all, what physicists *now* meant when they used the words 'physics' or 'physical science'. The discovery of the atom had caused little trouble. It was when research entered the sub-atomic realm that the difficulties had begun. They began when it was found that the behaviour of sub-microscopic particles, or some of it, simply did not fit into the classical framework. For there was, of course, no question of *abandoning* Newton's or Maxwell's laws. And yet within the framework of those laws this verified behaviour did not make sense.

Well, he was not here to give a history lesson. If there were any question of that, there were those among his hearers who could more fitly teach *him*. He was not going to take them through the history of how these difficulties had been solved for all, or nearly all, practical purposes. He was not going to talk about the two-hole or two-slit experiment with electrons. They would readily recall Heisenberg's uncertainty relation and Niels Bohr's principle of complementarity. For his purpose all that was needed at this stage was to point out that since about 1925 the teething troubles had been overcome by the working system known as quantum mechanics.

The price paid for this brilliant achievement, including as it did the virtual substitution of probability for causality as their basic principle, had been heavy; and he would have something more to say of that later. But at least, *at* that price, the goods had been delivered and the last word spoken on fundamental physical theory. So it was thought until quite recently. Yet now a new problem had arisen and one of which no solution was as yet in sight. Moreover, the new problem had a suspiciously familiar look about it. In the old days you took the atom as final; then you found that at certain energy-levels this atom of yours was unstable and subject to transformation. So you went deeper and discovered that the atom itself had components and an inner structure. Result: the Rutherford-Bohr planetary atom. But then again you found that, at certain energy-levels, the nucleus of the atom was itself unstable and the behaviour of the particles far from planetary. Your predictions had ceased to accord with your experiments. Result: quantum mechanics. And now? Now you were finding that at certain still higher energy-levels, and when extrapolated to very short distances—distances of the order of 10^{-13} cm. and less—what? Not exactly that your last haven of refuge had become unstable—because the relation of quantum mechanics to actuality was such that there was nothing to become unstable. But you were again finding—and for a physicist it was the acid test—that in these circumstances your predictions ceased to accord with your experiments. This was the situation as he saw it and it was one for which he did not think 'crisis' was too strong a word.

When the atom failed us—if he could be allowed the picturesque expression—we could dig into it and come at the electron, together with its now rapidly increasing family of brother particles; when the electron failed us, there was clearly no question of digging into it in a spatial sense and finding still smaller components. So you took refuge in mathematics and devised quantum mechanics. But now, if quantum mechanics was failing us, what was left? Experimentally, clearly nothing. For quantum mechanics dealt only with pure abstractions. The de Broglie-Schrödinger particles were mere mathematical 'points' and their waves mere waves of probability-distribution.

Perhaps he ought to try to expand a little what he had just said and, in doing so, he would ask their indulgence for the inevitable oversimplification. The quantum *theory*, then, as distinct from the quantum mechanics afterwards erected on it, had—as they knew—led to something like a dispute on the issue whether radiation, including the radiation known as light, must be thought of as consisting of waves or alternatively as a kind of rain of electro-magnetic corpuscles. He would shorten it all by simply saying that it was a dispute in which both parties had turned out to be right. In one context, or for some purposes, radiation must be treated as though it were continuous waves; in another context, and for other purposes, it must be treated as though it consisted of discrete bodies. Quantum mechanics had simply accepted this anomaly, treating it, some would say, as a final limitation imposed on human knowledge, others as an irrational feature inherent in the nature of reality.

But quantum mechanics had also accepted something else, another 'non-classical' principle to which he had so far barely alluded. This was, of course, the element of chance, or randomness—the incidence of apparently causeless irregularities alike in the behaviour of the supposed particles and in the individual wavelengths comprising the supposed 'field'. It dealt with these irregularities by applying the mathematical laws of probability.

Experimentally it was established that, though irregularities certainly existed, they were slight enough to cancel out, as it were, at the macroscopic level. Quantum mechanics accordingly dealt only with statistical averages. He need not dwell on the successes which the new method had achieved. They had only to look round at the amazing technological development of the last two or three decades.

Yet it was at this point that the problem to which he was seeking to draw attention really arose. He had threatened to oversimplify and he had already lived up to that warning. For he had described a series of physical events and had gone on to say that quantum mechanics dealt with those events by calculating their average outcome—making use for that purpose of abstract statistical laws of chance. One had something like the picture of an actuary employed by an insurance company. But from another point of view this was a completely misleading picture. Quantum mechanics was *totally* mathematical. In other words its micro-physical statements were statistical in some other and more absolute sense. For once they had been mathematically propounded, it was found impossible to *reinterpret* them in any way that could render them descriptive of actual 'sub-quantum' events; or even of an aggregate or average of such actual events. The limits imposed by quantum mechanics on our whole technique of observation actually prevented us from giving any *meaning*—in terms of physical observations—to statements *about* these supposed sub-quantum events.

This, said the lecturer, did not seem to matter as long as the results we wished to calculate did not depend on the assumed size—and, with that, the existence—of the micro-entity. It was when you needed to extrapolate the quantum theory to excessively small distances that the inconsistencies began to show up. He would not go into them; they were highly technical; involved as they were with linear equations, and with the prediction of infinite values for physical properties, such as the mass and the charge of the electron. The difficulties arose from the necessity, according to quantum theory, of assuming that elementary particles are mathematical points occupying no space at all. On the other hand, it was only by way of such an extrapolation that we seemed able to approach the crucial question for physics today: what keeps the nuclei of atoms together?

He hoped he had said enough to make his first point. To speak of the 'structure' of anything seemed to imply that it occupied space. How then could we begin to investigate, how could we speak, how could we even *think* of an 'internal' structure of the bodies with which quantum theory dealt? Yes. It was difficult. They knew how laymen got into difficulties with the quantum theory and quantum mechanics, because of their obstinate need to continue thinking in terms of those 'models' which the theory itself had expressly abandoned. His submission would be that that need was not quite the *pons asinorum* which trained physicists nowadays generally assumed, but that it remained— albeit in a concealed form—a lion in the path of further research and of the whole development of their science. This would involve his first saying something of that whole practice of thinking in terms of models, which had played such an active part in the development of classical physics, and even, in its early stages, of sub-atomic physics.

But there was something else he would like to say first. One thing that had been impressed on him many times, and in a way that was unforgettable, by the distinguished physicist with whom he had had the privilege of working was the necessity in their science of absolute open-mindedness. An open mind, a willing- ness to entertain the unfamiliar, the new, the untried hypothesis, the refusal to condemn even the shocking without investigation —this was the first scientific principle of all; it was this that constituted the scientific *spirit*, as distinct from scientific habit. The young lecturer broke into a disarming smile. In saying this, he realized that he was preaching to the converted; it might sound as if he was having the effrontery to advise the Physical Society to be scientific! Yet, in view of what he intended to say, he had not been able to resist it. He had not been able to resist it because he also retained so deep an impression of the other thing which his early guide had often said to him; how often the scientist did, in fact, fall short of this ideal! There was a very real tendency to accept as final and exclusive at least the *general* shape of the theories current in our own day. They had seen it, a few years ago, in the strong resistance that had been put up to any suggestion that the general theory of classical physics was of only limited application. Were they going to see it again today? He hoped not. Surely it had been proved often enough in the history of science that there were times, there were junctures, when the voice of nature, to which it was their duty to listen without any sub-conscious reservations, spoke in unexpected, in apparently self-contradictory, even in shocking ways. History, moreover, showed that that was the very phenomenon which hinted that a new advance was imminent. If men listened humbly to the great voice, the new advance would come—but only if they listened to *all* it said, and listened in the fullest sense of those words 'without prejudice'. To his own little stumbling voice this evening he was confident they would listen in that way and no other.

It was at this point in the evening that one of the visitors present, the lecturer's own invited guest seated in the front row, suddenly grew more alert. Not that his attention had exactly wandered. The reading he had undertaken since his last encounter with the Meggid, and indeed on the Meggid's persuasion, had enabled Burgeon to follow most of what had so far been said without too much difficulty. But it must be admitted that his attention had lately begun to flag a little. *Now* he had the pleasure of recognition to enliven it, as his mind went back to a long talk he had had with this interesting young man a few weeks ago. Kenneth Flume was the nephew of an old friend. Though Burgeon had known him slightly from boyhood, it was only on that evening that the two had, properly speaking, 'met' and, in doing so, had discovered how, underlying all their differences, of age, of background, of interests, of assumptions about most things that are important, they acknowledged one passionless passion in common. Now, by his choice of words, Flume was delicately, in his presence, bearing witness to it. Perhaps it was flattering; certainly it was touching; and the listener felt himself strangely and strongly drawn to the speaker.

To return, Flume continued, to this question of models. There was a feeling in many quarters that they should now be abandoned altogether. No single model had been devised, and none apparently could be, with which quantum mechanics would fit; and quantum mechanics was so effective, it was said, that there was no need for one anyway. Others took the opposite view; and one strong argument for it, which must appeal to all physicists, was this: how was it possible to make any substantial further advance without them? Fruitful research, if it was to have any directedness, any coherence, must be based on *some* new hypothesis, however tentative, and (they added) however mistaken. You had to have something to work on. In the history of science it had often been the ardent attempt to prove a new but false hypothesis which had led to the discovery of the new and true one. He instanced Kepler's almost accidental discovery of the ellipse as the true basis of planetary astronomy. How could any new theory ever swim into our ken if we continued to have simply no way whatever of representing to our minds what actually goes on at the sub-microscopic level? He personally felt that there was only one answer to that question; and this had led him to give some thought to the whole question of the nature and function of the model in the process of scientific enquiry.

The model was a moving system—nowadays generally a notional one only—of objects within the ordinary range of perception by the unaided sense, by means of which the mind represented to itself the operation of a natural process. Generally the process so represented was itself beyond the range of the unaided senses, because otherwise no model was needed. It was when the process was either too big or too small for the senses to perceive it as a whole that scientists had had to recourse to the model. Thus, to help us to grasp the working and proportions of the solar system, we imagined a collection of spherical objects varying in size from, say, a football to a pea, revolving round each other in some space not bigger than a fair-sized room. At the other end of the scale—when they had wanted to think about the molecular motions of gases, or the inner structure of the atom—it had been much the same. Billiard balls, for some reason, had been a strong favourite here. He suggested that there was another essential feature of the model, which had perhaps not yet been so fully appreciated. Characteristically, the model was a moving system of a kind which, given sufficient skill, *we could ourselves construct*. The objects we selected were of a size and nature that we could handle as well as perceive. The model system was accordingly one which we could at least *think* of ourselves as constructing. A moving system constructed by man is, of course, a machine, and classical physics, in the development of which the model played such a leading part, perhaps inevitably culminated in the general theory known as 'mechanical causality'.

'The reason,' said the lecturer, 'why I am troubling you with all this is that I am one of those who are convinced that, unless we do succeed in solving this problem of representation, there is no way forward for us. No doubt we shall improve in accuracy, we shall fill in some gaps; but of another leap forward, such as occurred with the transition from classical to nuclear physics, I see no prospect whatever. For in order to be led to *new* ideas, we really must be able to imagine—or at least apprehend in *some* way—what is actually happening. And that is just what, apparently, we have ceased to be able to do.

'I am anxious that, before we give up the struggle, before we settle down to the conviction that field and particle represent the last limit of what the human brain is capable of conceiving, we should seek to explore this problem of representation a little more exhaustively. At the moment, we have, on the one side, our quantum mathematics, to which the existence or non-existence of its subject-matter is a matter of indifference, and, on the other side, those models which we look like having to abandon. And there is no connection between them. Or, more precisely, there is only a *historical* connection between them. In this situation the only fruitful line of enquiry I can see, the only possible *starting*-point, is to ask ourselves the question: Is there some conceptual sphere which lies between mathematics at the one extreme and the "model" type of thinking at the other? Is there a mean between the zero-representation which charac-terizes the mathematical symbol and the solid, constructional representation aimed at by the model? In this connection, and to indicate one possible starting-point for such a line of enquiry, I would draw attention once more to the particular circumstances that have led up to the collapse of the model as a mental support for scientific research. It began when Niels Bohr con-vinced us that, if we insist on having a model at all, then we must have two complementary ones, which cannot both be used at the same time: the wave model and the interacting-particles model. Now you will notice that these two so-called models differ from each other in one important aspect. Only the second, the interacting-bodies one, answers to the definition, which I hazarded, of a model as a system which we could in theory our-selves construct. We do not think of ourselves as constructing *waves*; their structure—if structure is the right word—and their motions and interactions are an immediately "given" experience made available by nature herself, so that in this type of model, if we should so call it, we are using nature herself, macroscopic nature, nature as normally experienced, as our means of representing sub-microscopic nature. It is possible that this distinction may turn out to be an important one.

'But above all I ask myself if our predicament is not one which obliges us to look for help in any direction where it might conceivably be found. Would it not be wise, for instance, to pray in aid some of the results arrived at in other disciplines than our own? We could at least try the experiment. Here I will suggest one possibility, and I put it forward as an example only. There are those who have studied with some care the whole process of representation that normally goes on between the mind and nature. Forgive me if for a few moments I speak of matters of which I know almost nothing, and know even that from hearsay! I am told that the nature and function of the human imagination has received a lot of attention in the last few decades; that it has been examined as a mode of interaction between the observing mind and the observable—or conceivable—object, which underlies both thinking and perceiving. But that is not all. By some at least of those who have researched in that field it is claimed, I am told, that the element of imagination, which is present in a slight degree even in normal perception and normal thought, can be isolated, as it were, for the purpose of determining its attributes, and that when that is done there is a considerable measure of agreement about what is found. For example—once again I am told—imagination as such is especially adapted for apprehending a relation between a whole and its parts different from that of aggregation, and different again from any kind of relation envisaged by classical physics, but not altogether unknown in the organic realm. It has been said that imagination directly apprehends the whole as "contained" in the part, or as in some mode identical with it.

'Secondly, it is said to be characteristic of imagination that it apprehends spatial form, and relations in space, as "expressive" of non-spatial form and non-spatial relations. A third attribute which is claimed for it is that, operating as it is said to do, anteriorly to the kind of perception and thought which have become normal for fully conscious modern man, it functions at a level where observed and observer, mind and object, are no longer—or are not yet—spatially divided from one another; so that the mind, as it were, becomes the object or the object becomes the mind.

'Now it seems to me that the first two claims alone—if there is anything in them—*might* be of some significance in our problem. For this question of the actual relation between whole and part and the closely allied question of spatial relationships, and of the nature of space itself, is very much the heart of our matter. Perhaps, when we are considering the relation between field and particle—or rather, as at present, considering how to consider it—we should be rash to leave such claims altogether unexamined.'

Returning to more familiar ground, the lecturer said they would know he was not the only physicist who was being led by the recent developments to which he had referred to reflect on the whole treatment of space, both mathematical and non-mathematical, in physical theory. He supposed the overall goal of physics, apart from utilitarian considerations, was to determine, as precisely as possible, the structure of matter and, through that, the structure of the universe. To this end it had been consistently striving to resolve matter into its ultimate elements. Originally the chemical 'elements' had themselves been regarded as ultimate; but with the advance of science these had increased in number in a disconcerting way, as more and new elements were discovered. At the same time they were discovered to be unstable, because capable of changing into each other. It became necessary, therefore, to investigate the *structure* of the chemical element; and that search had soon become a search for elementary particles. With the triumph of the atomic theory the atom was for a time accepted as the elementary particle—until it, too, was found to be unstable, and capable of transformation. It was therefore assumed, rightly, that the atom was not, in fact, an elementary particle but a micro-object with a structure which itself called for investigation.

'Now, in our own time, the same process is being repeated with the sub-atomic particles, into which the structure of the atom has been resolved. There is the same menacing increase in their number; we have had to add to the original and, as it was hoped, ultimate electron, not only protons and neutrons, but positrons, neutrinos and many different kinds of mesons and hyperons. Nor is there any sign of an end to the process. We might have assumed from this symptom, even if we had not actually found, that the sub-atomic elementary particle would turn out itself to be unstable. In fact, we have found them capable—at very high energy-levels—of being transformed into each other or, in the case of the newer particles, of "decaying" into neutrons, protons and electrons. We have, moreover, to assume that these bodies can be "created" in collisions of other particles with nuclei. Putting it shortly, the new "elementary particle" turns out to be no more "ultimate" than did the atom into whose structure it combines, or than the chemical element into whose structure the atom itself combines.

'Logically, therefore, our next step can only be an investigation of the inner structure of the sub-atomic particle itself. But it is here that the difficulties I have been reminding you of this evening arise. My time is running out and I shall remind you now of one of them only—the awkward fact that, for mathematical purposes, what we at present regard as the elementary particles have to be deemed of zero size. This does seem to raise in an acute form the question, which has been raised by others before me and for other reasons, whether we are not being called on to revise our whole notion of space; or, if you prefer it, of space-time. But I would prefer, as far as possible, to simplify by leaving time out of the reckoning this evening.'

Maybe, he continued, they had not yet appreciated the full implications of introducing the 'field' concept at all into physical theory. That had already constituted a striking departure from the classical framework of the universe. Newtonian mechanics postulated that things were constituted of bodies interacting according to specified forces; and perhaps a Newtonian space had followed from those mechanics. But the whole scheme had been found inadequate by the end of the nineteenth century. They had had to introduce a new set of entities, the electric and magnetic fields. Now, the mode of existence of a 'body' had required that it be localized in some definite region of space, whereas the fields, consisting of energy without mass, had to be conceived of as *continuously* distributed throughout the whole of space. One could only speak tentatively and with great hesitation; but the sort of question that arose, for him, was: had they perhaps to abandon the assumption that *structure*, as such, was exclusively 'inner'—'inner' in terms of Newtonian space? Was it nonsense to conceive of something like an 'external' structure? Alternatively, or implied, if the increasingly constricted hunt after the inner structure of matter was not to be abandoned altogether, were they obliged to take in conceptually, in addition to the $3N$

dimensional space of their equations (to which no sort of actuality could be attributed) a—what should he say?—a negative, or perhaps a potential, space, for which they had no model and therefore, as yet, no equations; for in the history of science up to now the equations had always followed the model, even if they subsequently abandoned it? That such a space would have some very unfamiliar features was not in itself an objection; for everything suggested, as he had tried to remind them, that it would be of little use in their present predicament unless it did. If they hoped ever in any way to imagine the kind of field which is represented 'mathematically' by the ψ field of Schrödinger, it might involve, nay, it *must* involve, learning to think, in an unaccustomed way, of such fundamental relations as inner and outer, centre and periphery. Actually it had happened at about the time when he himself was first venturing on this highly speculative flight, that his attention was drawn to those studies in the psychology of imagination to which he had briefly alluded. He had mentioned them this evening on the footing that, in a really tight place, any way out might be worth trying; and that, however unlikely it might look, it was better to try the only one in sight than to sit still and do nothing. But he perhaps owed to that accident a notion that had also occurred to him, that the elementary particle for which they sought might be conceivable, might some day be conceived, as the detectable moment of transition from structure, or potential structure, in negative space to ordinary 'inner' structure in Newtonian, three-dimensional space—with the electric and magnetic fields affording perhaps some slight tantalizing evidence of the anterior process leading up to it. It might, he suggested, be in some such direction as this that they would have to look for the answer to what he himself regarded as the crucial question for physics: What keeps the nuclei of atoms together?

The lecturer concluded with a further apology to his audience for the highly speculative nature of some of the considerations he had placed before them. If he was right in calling the present state of physics a 'crisis'—and he was not the first to do so—then it might well be that any further advance depended on the discovery of new entities—of entities as new to contemporary physics as the electric and magnetic fields had been to classical physics. He himself did not think—and here again he was not alone—that there was any foreseeable future at all for their science, unless they at least *explored* new ways of thinking. Whether there was any value in the particular suggestions he had made would be decided by others than himself and he hoped, up to a point, would be discussed in the time that remained to them this evening.

ELEVEN

Flume sat down to the accompaniment of an uncertain volume of applause and a rather anxious Chairman rose to his feet to offer conventional thanks for a paper which everyone, whatever he might think of the lecturer's conclusions, must certainly have found both stimulating and thought-provoking. He then declared the meeting open for questions and discussion.

Burgeon, joining in the applause, was glad of the moment's relaxation which it afforded him. For if his attention had been close almost from the beginning, it had become, from the moment when Flume had referred to those 'other disciplines', close to the point of breathlessness. There had been, moreover, a sort of tension in it. It was as if—he reflected afterwards, borrowing from the lecture itself to clothe his thought—something in the nature of a 'field' had been created at that point, filling the space and bridging the gap between himself and the platform. There was an uncomfortably dead silence lasting for about half a minute, while the Chairman directed enquiring and encouraging glances round the small hall. At last a querulous voice from the back enquired:

'Is the speaker not going to tell us anything more about this negative space with which he has left us? He hasn't told us much yet—unless we are to infer from something else he said that every part of it contains the whole!'

The lecturer, who appeared somewhat embarrassed, began replying that he feared it would really take them too far and into realms which were admittedly still purely speculative. He had not intended to do more than introduce the idea . . .

He was interrupted by another member of the audience, who spoke in a way that hinted a philosophical turn of mind. Burgeon had the feeling that his motive was rescue.

'I,' he said, 'would like to ask another question, which may have some bearing on the last one. When he was speaking of the structure of matter, Mr. Flume reminded us that *structure* implied space—Newtonian space as he called it—because it implied size. Would he perhaps regard this relationship of necessity as a reciprocal one—so that the existence of space also implies some sort of structure?'

The lecturer brightened up, as he came forward to reply. It was an interesting question, he said. He was inclined to think his answer would be yes. He had used the term 'Newtonian space'; it would perhaps have been better to say 'Cartesian space'. He had in mind a hint dropped by David Bohm to the effect that the invention of the Cartesian co-ordinates had marked a crucial moment in the history of mathematical physics, determining the whole of its subsequent history. Perhaps the co-ordinates were not as inevitable as we all assumed. Bohm had suggested that it was not a 'natural' idea, but that there was, on the contrary, a certain arbitrariness about it. Our ordinary direct experience both of space and of time was not Cartesian but topological— inside and outside, above and below, before and after, etc. But at a certain point in the history of science we had made an abstraction that was not forced on us by nature, by introducing the precise, but limiting, Cartesian co-ordinates.

'And every inch we have advanced since then,' said the first querulous, and now definitely irritated, voice, 'has depended on them.'

'I know,' said the lecturer patiently. 'And in a way that is Bohm's point, too. I said they were arbitrary. I did not say they were unnecessary. Of course all our advance has depended on them. But the question I have tried to raise this evening was whether any *further* advance can do so. All this arose out of the first question I was asked. I think it possible—and this, if I understand him rightly, is Bohm's suggestion—that our habit of beginning, as it were, with space and time, as if they were existents, and then planting a number of objects in them, may be traceable to the Cartesian innovation. Whereas it would perhaps be possible to begin with the process itself—in this case the structural process—and look at the order of events, as it were, from their own point of view. We should then perhaps find that the relation between structure and space *is* reciprocal and that it is not the inevitable nature of our minds, but the Cartesian abstraction, which makes us find the notion of space without structure less absurd than the notion of structure without space.'

'Really,' said a louder voice from a different part of the hall, 'we cannot possibly deal with this sort of thing in this Society. We are not a philosophical body. We are scientists. It is all very well to talk of open-mindedness, but surely that does not mean that scientists must waste their time chasing every unsupported speculative hare that is put up to them! They would have no time for serious work if they did. Where are your equations— if you really have something to say to us—where are your predictions based on them and by what experiments were they verified ?'

At this point there was a slight murmur of approval, punctuated by a few pointed *Hear! Hear!s* and followed by a tendency in the audience towards indulgence in private whispered conversations. The Chairman rose and did his best to smooth things down. The question, he said, of the place of speculative hypotheses in scientific investigation, and of the stage in their growth at which it was right to air them, was an interesting one. He could not altogether agree with the last speaker. It was a matter of discretion, wasn't it? Some unsupported hypotheses had subsequently turned out to be right. Others, alas—and, as he suspected, the great majority—had not. Even the lucky guess had sometimes been unlucky in being advanced too soon, that is, before the general climate of scientific opinion and the pace of advance was ready for them. Prout's speculations, published half a century before the work of J. J. Thompson, on the existence of a common sub-atomic matter, had not been of much practical use, and that had been Prout's misfortune. It might well be that our lecturer this evening was ahead of his time in the same way. If so, there was not much they could do about it. The science of physics was, after all, quantitative, and he felt some sympathy with the last comment they had heard, though he for one would have been very sorry indeed to miss this thought-provoking paper. It was, of course, for the lecturer himself to reply, if he wished.

The lecturer said he would like to attempt a reply—though there was some risk of its involving another entire lecture. The Chairman would have to stop him if that looked like happening. First, then, as to the suggestion that the time was not yet ripe for advancing speculative hypotheses of the kind he had been indulging in—it seemed to him to depend on one's estimate of the gravity of the crisis. Time would show. He certainly thought that a good many physicists did underestimate the significance of the collapse of the classical model; and that the positivist solution of renouncing the model, or any substitute for it, altogether and for all time was a surprisingly light-hearted one.

Then, as to the demand for equations—of course, they must come. And no doubt they would be developed on purely mathematical lines. But you had to have a start. The equations they used now had themselves originated in the application of thought to some kind of model. Thompson himself had still had the classical model to work on and, without it, would presumably never have achieved the very results which had ended in that model's being superseded. He thought this could hardly be stressed too heavily. But his point now was that perhaps the classical model had not been superseded *enough*. This, he suspected, was why Bohm, for instance, had begun to look more closely at the Cartesian co-ordinates and their part in the history of science. The lecturer went on to maintain that it was, above all, the introduction of the co-ordinates that had made possible the development of mechanics and, with that, the acceptance by science of an overall model of mechanical causality—which was the *constructional* model *par excellence*. What they were now trying to do, apparently, was to discard that model from their thinking, while retaining the absolute supremacy *for all purposes and in all contexts* of its father, the Cartesian co-ordinates. Would this, in the long run, work? He submitted that the question was at least worth asking. Putting it picturesquely, might they not find that their mathematics was still haunted by the ghost of the model their theory had liquidated? Perhaps that was one of the reasons why some physicists today found themselves talking, to their own surprise, of 'ghost particles'.

As to the nature of the equations (and here he again became diffident and apologetic), possibly he was unwise to attempt to say anything. His own prowess as a mathematician was limited. But he had been challenged and did not wish to funk the issue altogether. Results, he suggested, might be yielded by a developmental comparison of the mathematics stemming from the two types of model he had distinguished—by placing the contribution made by what he would call the particle idea to quantum mathematics side by side with the contribution of the wave idea—comparing, as it were, Heisenberg/Bohr with de Broglie/Schrödinger. As to the possibility of an entirely new topological approach, such as Bohm had envisaged, he would say nothing—except that there was, in fact, a topological mathematics, of which he himself knew almost nothing except that it existed.

Flume went on now to the point that had been made of the essentially quantitative nature of physics, and here Burgeon had more difficulty in following him. He began with an apologetic concession (and Burgeon had a feeling that these were getting rather too frequent), after which he rather humbly submitted that the line between the quantitative and the qualitative, as the proper subject-matter of physics, had perhaps been more sharply drawn than it would bear. For a long time the physicist had assumed that all quality as such was subjective. He had nevertheless also assumed that observed changes of quality are caused by changing relations between objective entities; and on this footing he had pursued untroubled his search for some basic entity which itself never changes. Now it was beginning to be argued that both the assumptions and the search must be abandoned. Flume reverted to the point in his lecture at which he had mentioned the two-way interaction of field and particle and then (as far as Burgeon understood him) he seemed to be saying that the 'probabilistic' interpretation of nature, as distinct from the 'causal' one, implied that they had underrated the importance of the 'macroscopic level'. Quantitative irregularities at the microscopic or submicroscopic level, *when dealt with statistically*, were in effect being treated as *qualities* at the higher level. It had proved impossible to pursue indefinitely the inveterate practice of deducing the laws governing larger-scale phenomena from the laws—if any—governing the behaviour of micro-objects—if any. They had simply not succeeded in finding a 'basic' micro-entity which was incapable of changing its mode of being, that is, of changing *qualitatively*, changing into another entity.

He thought the same conclusion followed from the apparently irreducible phenomenon of 'random' fluctuations. Either they must abandon for good and all any attempt to determine the causes and origin of these fluctuations or—and he again took the example of life insurance—they must assume that they came from qualitatively new entities to be looked for in some new domain altogether.

'Mr. Chairman,' said a new voice from the back of the hall, 'all this is very exciting, but there is one thing Mr. Flume has not yet succeeded in explaining to us. Why is it necessary? Anyone would think, from all this talk of a crisis, that the science of physics was in a bad way. But is that so? Has any other science advanced so far and so fast in the last forty years? I seem to have read something about satellites. We are obviously only at the beginning of what we shall learn from them: but I only mention them as an example. Quantum mechanics was good enough, when it came to the problem of developing nuclear power, which may well transform the entire face of the world in the next forty years. Does the lecturer think we should have done better if we had adopted the peculiar methods he seems to be advocating? What is the matter? What is it all about? He keeps on suggesting that we are faced with an almost insoluble problem. I would have thought—and I believe most physicists feel the same—that we had solved the main problem and that the development of quantum mechanics—which is apparently almost a dirty word in his vocabulary—is a matter for congratulating ourselves, and of course the great names to whom we owe it, rather than for racking our brains to find holes to pick in it.'

He sat down, and the lecturer came forward to the front of the platform and for some seconds remained silent. Burgeon thought he knew very well how he was feeling; asking himself, no doubt, whether he should try and say it all over again, or just give up! At last Flume began by trying to re-state his attitude to quantum mechanics and the statistical approach generally. He really did not think he underrated the achievement they represented or failed in admiration for the great names. On the contrary, he rather thought it was his very admiration for the work of de Broglie that had determined his choice of a profession. To return once more to the old analogy, he no more criticized these methods or advocated their abandonment than a physiologist, engaged on research into the causes of death, criticized the insurance companies for treating death as a contingency to be calculated by the laws of chance. Perhaps he had not made it clear enough . . . (He paused for a moment to collect himself and, when he proceeded, struck out a new line.) Might he return once more to this vexed question of models? Almost from the birth of physics, physical thought had employed, fundamentally, the type of model he had called 'constructive'. When, that was, it employed a model at all. It might be that this had resulted in the development of a method apt for construction, apt for all

137

technological purposes, but not so apt for knowledge. There was even a dispute now whether the word 'knowledge' really *meant* anything more than technological effectiveness. This was to abolish altogether any distinction between theoretical science and applied science. By 'knowledge' he himself meant knowledge of actuality. If you confined yourself to predicting that certain observable phenomena would follow certain other observable phenomena—whether the others were naturally occurring or experimentally produced; if you felt happy to say—as had often been said—that, as far as you were concerned, the atom had no existence when it was not being observed; if you accepted the restrictive interpretation of nature, according to which transitions from one state to another are fully described by the initial and final stages and nothing can be said either now or for ever about intervening events, then he for one would think that your game should be called technology rather than science—a word which, after all, began life as the Latin for 'knowledge'. He thought this was accurate. He did not intend it to be insulting. He knew too many excellent physicists who whole-heartedly accepted the restrictive interpretation. For him, however, it came down to the question whether one wished to go on being a scientist—or was content to remain, in essence, an engineer. He personally was not and it was to any others who happened to feel the same that his remarks this evening had been primarily addressed.

Flume was greeted at this point with a slight and scattered murmur of applause, though the answer as a whole had not succeeded in arresting a tendency, which had become increasingly apparent, for individual members to tiptoe cautiously to the swing doors and disappear through them as silently as their imperfect lubrication permitted. The Chairman again looked enquiringly round the hall with the ill-concealed hope that no one would respond. But it was not to be. Even as he gathered himself to rise and close the meeting, the philosophically disposed member, who had come to the rescue before, anticipated him by rising again himself.

'I really think,' he said, 'that we have not come nearly as far to meet Mr. Flume as his lecture deserved. For instance, I find myself in very full agreement with what he said about the absolute necessity of hypotheses of some sort, to enable research to guide and direct—he might well also have said to *select*—its experiments. And I believe that, in the long run, this is as true for applied science as it is for theoretical science. It is true that the scientific papers we read to each other are carefully arranged to suggest that we first made a lot of experiments without an idea in our heads and then, by looking at them in an unhurried and objective way, were forced to the "conclusions" that we set out at the end of the paper. It would usually be more honest to set out those conclusions at the beginning, since they were, in fact, the guess or theory we had in mind in conducting the observations. J. S. Mill's so-called inductive logic has much to answer for. I believe it is largely a fiction and, if we want to know what mental processes really underlie the process of scientific research, we should take a look at, for instance, Karl Popper's *Logic of Scientific Discovery*.

'In this respect I cannot see that the substitution of mathematics for actuality helps us much. If it is impossible to embark on a bunch of experiments without the remotest idea of what we are looking for, surely it is at least equally impossible to look round *directly* for new equations, to play about blindly with all sorts of mathematical manipulations in the hope that one of them may lead to something. The plain fact is that there must be a model, or at the least a concept of *some* sort, in the researching mind, before any research can be done. It is by the light of this picture in our minds that we choose and arrange our experiments and observations; it is from this that we deduce the predictions by which we subsequently test its validity. The results that follow may be positive or negative, but they are at least *results*, and at least we have an expectation to compare them with. Without something of the sort we could do nothing.

'Now I cannot comment in any way on Mr. Flume's remarks on the psychology of imagination. But I think in fairness we must concede one point to him. It has been widely admitted— among those who are at work on the general *theory* of scientific discovery—that theory begins as guess-work—which is a shorter way of saying that the origin of hypothesis is imaginational or inspirational—and that the stricter process of making deductions from the theory, and testing these by prediction and experiment, is only secondary. I see nothing inherently unreasonable there-fore—though I put it no higher—in the question he has raised. That question, as I understand it, is not whether imagination can be used in forming theories on which to base research—for we know that it *is* already used—but whether it can be used *directly* in some way and not through the medium of what we call models. That is all I wished to say.'

All this would no doubt have interested Burgeon very much indeed if he had been listening to it. But he was otherwise engaged. Convinced of the importance, at least on a long view, of what was going on and increasingly aware that Flume was showing signs of weariness, his own thoughts had wandered off to the Meggid. Insensibly they turned into a strenuous inner cry for help. He had perhaps never felt a sharper longing for the strength which his mentor's presence could add. He did not get as far as considering what he could do if the Meggid came in answer to his call; to attempt speech himself in such a gathering would be the wildest presumption, and at an earlier stage, when the possibility occurred to him, he had at once ruled it out. Yet the cry went on going up from within him.

And now—a minute or so before the last speaker finished and resumed his seat—Burgeon became aware, from certain subtle symptoms which experience had taught him to recognize, of the Meggid's near approach. With confidence he expected his immediate presence. Yet nothing happened! It was bewildering. It was disconcerting. As certainly as if he had felt the wind of some spatial passing, he knew that the Meggid had indeed approached him—and had passed him by.

When he looked back afterwards he could never be quite sure whether the little incident that followed had actually taken place in the phenomenal world, or whether he had been led to form his own physical picture of another's subjective experience. Standing on the edge of the platform and about to speak, Flume raised, or it seemed that he raised, both his arms and stretched them outward above his head. At the same time he parted his legs and stood for an instant with a wide expanse between his feet. In that instant Flume yawned—yawned as Burgeon had never seen a man yawn in public before, without even the shadow of an effort to conceal it, unless its unusually brief duration betokened such an effort. The whole thing was over nearly as soon as it began; and the lecturer was starting already on what it soon became apparent was his final reply to the whole discussion.

It was late, he said, but he had been accused in the course of the discussion of not having said enough on certain points, and he really felt he must make one final attempt to set his position in a clearer light. If there was one thing that physical enquiry could claim to have established—or, as some would say, had been forced to admit—it was that everything in nature is in a perpetual state of transformation. He suggested that this was the fundamental difference between classical and modern physics. For the older physicists transformation had been essentially a *qualitative* phenomenon. Together with all natural process that can be perceived with the unaided senses, they had regarded it as the province of the other sciences, while it remained their own special task to seek for the stable basis, the stable entities, which persisted, themselves unchanged, through all these transformations. This fundamental aim, once universally accepted, was now being called in question. He had tried to recapitulate some of the recent developments that had unsettled it. The concept of 'fields' had perhaps been the Trojan Horse. It had had to be introduced even before the end of the classical period, but it was not really classical. It really meant abandoning the old assumption that the laws governing large-scale phenomena are to be deduced from those governing matter at the microscopic level. Thus, it had turned out to be at least as true to say that the behaviour of the particle was determined by the field as it was to say that the nature of the field was determined by the behaviours of particles. Then there was the discovery of the element of randomness— chance—alike in the behaviour of the particle and in the fluctuations that characterized, or perhaps *were*, the field. The existence of these low-level irregularities was—there seemed no possibility of getting away from it—inseparable from what appeared, at the higher level where the irregularities balanced out, as quality. This ran counter to the no less fundamental principle of classical physics, that the qualitative is always reducible to microscopic entities and events capable of precise quantitative measurement. The root-question was, did all this involve abandoning altogether the ancient, the traditional and, yes, the honourable quest for stable entities?

'Are you *going* to abandon it?' he asked them abruptly. 'But you have already abandoned it, in renouncing the concept of causality. Are you going to abandon it? You have already abandoned it, in renouncing the concept of the continuity of motion, without which the process of transformation itself is inconceivable to you. What is physics at all, if it is not the study of those processes by which some one thing comes from other things in the past and gives rise in its turn to yet other things in the future? This whole study is being taken away from you—by yourselves. Because you have chosen to deny, even while you continue out of habit to affirm, the transformation which is nature, nature herself is taken away from you. The actuality of your micro-objects disappears in the process of "renormalization", and the actuality of your waves into mere curves of probability-distribution in a ψ field.'

The speaker paused a moment. From the moment when he altered to 'you' the 'we' and 'they' he had been employing up to now most of the audience had seemed disposed to fix their gaze on the floor. Burgeon, who had been observing him closely since he began speaking again, continued to do so with increasing interest. There had been a noticeable change in Flume's bearing. It was not only that all traces of his former fatigue had disappeared. It was not only that he was speaking now with exceptional animation. It was more than that. There was something in the eyes—a blaze of noon—that suggested a man almost more wide awake than he himself could bear. Surely there could no longer be any doubt of it! Surely—and, with a complex emotion compounded of astonishment, triumph (for nothing of the sort had been recorded in Karo's case) and just the faintest imaginable pang of jealousy, Burgeon understood that now, in that hall, it was the Meggid himself who was speaking—and not from the audience!

Nevertheless the speaker reverted for a time to his former mode of address. 'We find a thing in being,' he said—'very well, our vocation as physicists is to enquire what other things it comes from, and how; and to what other things it will give rise. Are we to surrender that vocation? Do we remain medievally content with "creation and destruction operators" or, coyly avoiding the *word* "creation", go on saying that the number of particles has been "increased by zero + 1"? That was not the attitude that brought about the scientific revolution. And chance! Do we simply shrug our shoulders when we come across it? That was not the gesture of our predecessors. For them the phenomenon of the random, the fortuitous, the unexplained, was a challenge to seek out its causes in some new, hitherto unexplored domain.

'I ask again: Will *you* be the first to abandon the quest for stable entities, for the untransformed that persists through transformations to bring them about? Is this to be the *trahison*

des clercs for which the twentieth century will one day be in-
famous? Do you recite it *in your hearts*—that ultramontane creed
of the positivists, that men can only ever observe what they
already know how to observe? And what if Galileo, too, had
been among the faithful?

'Or will you still follow your vocation and seek the causes of
transformation in a new domain—in a domain which must con-
tain the field as the field contains the particle—and yet, at the
same time, be found *within* the nucleus, as the nucleus was found
within Prout's and Dalton's atom?

'Of the method and the thought-forms needed for research in
such a domain we can say nothing, for we as yet know nothing.
But we do know that they must be as apt for that domain as the
constructive model, and the thought-forms based on it, were apt
for the researches of classical physics. Some of you smiled when
I drew attention to the psychology of imagination. Others looked
embarrassed. I do not say it was the right suggestion; but
neither do I think it was an absurd one. Others chose to be
sarcastic about a space in which the part contains the whole, or
the centre the periphery. Yet the de Broglie relation itself is not
generally treated as a matter for sarcasm, nor the accepted principle that a single sharply defined wave must occupy the whole of
space. Is it mere folly to suggest that we are being forced to
cultivate a mode of thought capable of grasping such a relation
between whole and part? Or a mode of space itself which we
have not yet apprehended, leading us perhaps to the source from
which space itself originated?'

Flume paused again and for a moment it seemed that he had
finished. But he remained firmly on his feet, while he deliberated.

'Yes,' he said, at last, 'I will ask one question more and then
I shall have done. What *kind* of source can there be for the complex interacting rhythms of energy, of which we now find that
the physical universe consists? What other can it be than a
system of non-spatial relationships between hierarchies of energetic beings? And how can we obtain access to their realm,
unless we learn somehow to think of them without the help of
models, without constructive models, without nature-models,
yes, and also without the poetic and the theological models of a
bygone age?

'Perhaps that will necessarily involve ceasing to think *of*
them, and beginning, instead, to think their activity itself.

Perhaps it will involve so thinking that their energy, transformed, becomes our thought. Perhaps it is the same as saying unless we learn to hear them speaking directly to us—or through us.'

As soon as Flume finished speaking and, before he had resumed his seat, the Chairman took advantage of the unwonted lateness of the hour to close the meeting with a very brief and perfunctory word of thanks. Members of the audience, looking at their watches, quickly sought the door, and Flume himself, when Burgeon went up to congratulate him, seemed anxious to get away.

'Well,' he said nervously, as they went out together into the street, 'I have done for myself, I suppose! I don't quite know what came over me at the end.'

Burgeon looked at the young man and perceived at once that he was feeling small and depressed—as he himself had felt depressed and small after the Meggid's intervention in that long talk with Chevalier on board the liner.

'I'm not so sure of that,' he replied. 'I'm not so sure. For a time perhaps—but it may soon work out the other way. Things are moving pretty fast, aren't they? I have the feeling that quite a lot is going to happen quite soon that may incline some of those ladies and gentlemen to remember some of the things you said with no small surprise.'

'But I do rather wonder,' he added, when Flume made no reply, 'whether you were wise to talk about imagination.'

'Why! I thought that was just the very thing you—'

'Oh, not the *thing*! I mean the word. If you want to persuade your people to begin thinking about the relation between part and whole that is actually *there* in nature, you will have to find an impressive scientific name—*holomerism*, for instance, or *holomeristics*, or *centroperipherism*—something of that sort. I suppose that sounds like donnish sarcasm,' he added, as Flume again made no reply, 'and if I had said it ten years ago it would have been. But I have come to accept that sort of necessity as a simple truth which there is no point in cavilling at. Besides' (and he thought of the Meggid), 'when it comes to finding odd new names for what has been better named elsewhere, I am probably in no position to throw stones.'

The two walked on in silence till they came to Flume's bus stop. 'Just now,' Flume said at last, 'for some reason I feel desperately tired. I'm not sure I've taken in what you've been saying. But I should very much like to see you again fairly soon and talk the whole thing over.'

'Not more than I should,' said Burgeon, as he took out his diary.

TWELVE

It is unfortunately not possible, because it is still much too early, to say what delayed effect Flume's address and the discussion that followed it produced in the minds of his audience. Burgeon himself, whenever this question occurred to him, used to reflect that the most lasting impression would probably be found to have been made on some of those who had reacted most violently against it. How often it had been his own experience, in putting forward any novel and far-reaching idea, that the man who appeared to respond quickly and even sympathetically did so because he had not really taken it in. Meet him a few months later and he had forgotten all about it. Another, who opposed you—perhaps angrily—at every step of your argument, did so precisely because he was receiving it into depths that might subsequently digest it. Meet *him* a few months later, and you might well hear him putting forward your case, or something like it, as his own!

In any case this chronicle is mainly concerned with the illumination, or partial illumination, of the man Burgeon; and when it has been brought up to date by recording—so far as their nature permits of verbal reproduction—one or two more of those encounters with the Meggid, which are its principal justification, its task will be concluded.

One effect, however, which that memorable evening did produce must certainly be mentioned. It altered the whole hitherto fairly superficial relation between Burgeon and Flume. They met as arranged and then decided to meet again. They felt drawn together. In the course of a number of conversations he had with the young man Burgeon found it coming naturally to him to relate much, indeed, nearly all, of what he had learned from the Meggid, though he said nothing at first of the source. He hesitated over this and felt some compunction; but it was the easier to refrain because, in the course of the years, the information that had come to him from the Meggid and his own thoughts and reflections had become so inextricably involved with one another that it was almost impossible to disentangle them. He had expected—and so it proved—that Flume would listen attentively and would himself contribute on such subjects as the mystery of transformation in nature and its bearing on evolution and the theory of evolution. The background-thought from which the lecture clearly sprang had made that more than probable. What surprised him was the immediate interest that Flume displayed in much else that, as we have seen, had been preoccupying him with the Meggid's help. The historical, and even dogmatic, aspect which had held the stage through so much of that long talk with Grimwade and Chevalier—this, he had taken for granted, would be outside the range of Flume's interests. He was wrong. It was Flume himself, probing and following an incidental reference, who dragged out of him not only the substance but also a good deal of the detail of what had passed between the three of them on the liner.

Above all, Flume was fascinated by what Burgeon, or rather the Meggid in him, had revealed of the Council of Constantinople and the consequent elimination of spirit as a valid category of thought. You would have thought he had been waiting for it. At last, he said, somebody had explained to him the origin of classical physics, that concrete-bedded apparatus of interpretation which was so out of harmony with all that nuclear physics was now forcing on their attention and so ominously blocking its further advance. To Burgeon himself this was not nearly so obvious; and it led to what was perhaps the most interesting of all the discussions that took place between them. Here again it was *Flume* who pointed out the significance of that authoritative precept—in an age when authority counted and could be enforced—laid on the human spirit throughout Western Christendom, to deny to itself any participation in the creative spirit that informed the world of nature, about which it was so soon to grow curious. Severed from the start from every link with the world around it, except the link through sense-perception, set apart from and outside of the inner being of the world that it was struggling to know, what else could it do but devise a constructive model of it? And then more and more models! For the model presupposed the severance, and that was precisely what had been enjoined on the enquiring Western mind by the tenth Canon.

Interested as he was however, and quick to take the point, Flume showed no disposition to linger over it or to enter into further historical studies. It was the imminent *collapse* of classical physics, and with that of the whole 'model' approach to natural phenomena out of which it had grown, that really concerned him; and the question of what was to take its place. It was this that he wanted to pursue. And in this, of course, Burgeon could not so easily accompany him. On his side Burgeon gained much from their exchanges. The effort to expound to Flume the little that he felt he knew carried his own thoughts farther; they were clarified and deepened by the effort he was making to resume them. In making it, he found again, as he had found before, that they were mostly of the kind that cannot really be held in the *memory* at all, but must rather be re-created from within each time afresh. In addition to all this there were facts and, as we have seen, insights which he actually *learned* from his friend.

There was, however, one point whereon Flume had touched in his lecture and again in the ensuing discussion, upon which neither of them seemed able to get much light. Burgeon had never been able to understand how chance itself could be subject to 'laws'. He simply accepted, because he was told and believed it, that there were, in fact, laws of probability—laws of which a severely practical use was made, not only in applied physics, but in everyday matters such as the actuarial calculations on which the premium rates for life and accident insurance are based. Yet it had never made any sense to him. It seemed to involve a contradiction in terms. Moreover, it entailed certain particular consequences which he had always found equally puzzling. Thus, if there was a 'law' of some kind in operation, which tended to regularize a series of chance alternatives (the toss of a coin, for instance), it seemed to follow that a penny that had performed the unlikely feat of falling tails up, say ten times in succession, must be more likely to fall heads up the next time than it had been on the first toss. He was assured by those who knew that this was not the case, and that the chances for the eleventh toss were still exactly even. At what point then, and how, did the law operate? He had long given it up.

All this he confessed to Flume, when they began to discuss it, and it must be admitted that he did not succeed in getting much satisfaction. Flume at once made over again the point he had already made in his lecture, namely, that because a sequence of events is found to be subject to the laws of probability, we are not entitled to infer that the sequence is 'random' in the sense of being entirely uncaused. In the case, for instance, of insurance calculations no one suggests that deaths or accidents are uncaused. It is merely that their causes are extremely complex and lie in another domain altogether from the one we are dealing with. We know how many will die tomorrow, but we do not know who.

Burgeon stopped him. 'I see all that,' he said, 'but it does not meet my difficulty. Except to this extent: that *if* you are wrong, and *if* some of the other physicists are right in holding that there is such a thing as "pure" randomness, it would be even more mystifying that the same laws of probability should govern "pure" randomness as have been found to govern the "causes-in-another-domain" type of randomness. It looks as if I shall have to give it up.'

It was this conversation that finally determined Burgeon to seek once more the Meggid's guiding hand, or rather his pointing finger. Having formed the clear intention to do so, he began to consider how to formulate some particular question. But then a doubt came to him as to whether this was any longer the right course. True, he had asked questions in the past and received what seemed to be answers; but the exchanges, when they came, had never taken quite the form he had expected. There was always some element of surprise which made him feel that the Meggid took his own way. And then, on the last four occasions, the Meggid had come unannounced; and, on the last of all, not to himself at all but to another.

Whether, on the occasion now to be recorded, the Meggid once more came unasked, or whether the mere intention he had formed had operated as an appeal, was a question which Burgeon, when he came to consider it afterwards, did not think it necessary to pursue. The Meggid came. Once again the manner of his coming, and of his dealing, was new and unexpected, was even disconcerting. In the first place, it was at night, instead of at the more usual early-morning hour. And then, this time he made it clear that he had no information to impart. This time it was Burgeon himself who was to do the thinking which was also a 'speaking'. When I was last with you, said the Meggid, there was a matter whereof we had hardly spoken as yet, of which I beckoned you to think further. You have done so, and you have read and studied a little. Tell me what you have found.

It may be tedious, but is perhaps advisable, to repeat once more—that the dialogue-form is a kind of travesty of what actually passed between Burgeon and the Meggid. That is the somewhat undignified penalty that has to be paid for putting into words drawn from ordinary experience (and there are, after all, no other words) an experience that is not ordinary, inasmuch as it is beyond, or rather behind language, taking place in the realm whence the very faculty of transforming experience into words is derived. In the same mode of travesty, but not otherwise, one could say that this time Burgeon felt himself *in statu pupillari*— almost as though he were being set an examination paper—the type of paper employed in some places of learning and called 'collections'. He strove to do his best. Collecting his thoughts at such short notice, it was only those which had impressed themselves most deeply that now came to his mind.

I seem to myself, he said, to have found it again—the same fruitless effort to solve the problem of transformation without looking to the transforming agent. And with the same result: the artificial birth, and the frenzied pursuit, of *pairs* of concepts, pairs at once incompatible and counter, cunningly designed, it almost seems, to *hide* the very truth which the mind is striving to reach with their help. And I have thought that I detected behind these ideas, behind that inveterate habit of thought, the two adversaries whose natures you disclosed to me. You first did so, when I was preoccupied with a very different kind of transformation—the transformation of character—and had been offered the choice between punishment on the one hand and physic on the other—or so I thought. Later, with your help I saw them again, standing now behind 'heredity' and 'environment'— those twin concepts, at once antagonists and allies, with the aid of which my fathers have sought, and my brothers are still seeking so desperately, to construct an idea of 'evolution'. It is through you I have seen that what they thus construct is almost by definition no evolution at all, because it is no transformation; because it is only an idea of continuity plus an idea of substitution. Continuity without change and change only by substitution.

And now I have found them again in the domain to which you pointed me. Or can I be wrong? Yet I do not think so. This time —because that is the nature of the domain—they stand almost naked before me. Not something that is continuous, but mere continuity itself with no attributes; not something that is substituted, but mere substitution itself—substitution of one nothing for another nothing! Wave and particle—is it indeed the false Preserver and the false Destroyer who have riveted those obsessions on the growing-point of man's enquiring spirit?

It will be noticed that, in spite of his instructions, Burgeon had found himself unable to avoid putting his last observation in question form; and, if the question remained unanswered, he had at least the feeling that the Meggid was not dissatisfied. He wondered if he could now hope for any light to be thrown on the mystery of chance, which had been preoccupying himself and Flume. But the Meggid withdrew from him for a time; and almost immediately he fell asleep.

He awoke, abruptly, with the impression that the Meggid had already been addressing him for some time; so abruptly indeed, and yet so completely, that he seemed to be picking up the conclusion of a sentence, of which he had missed the start. And this, so far as it can be put into words, was what the Meggid was saying:

. . . regularity and irregularity. The regular is the *finished* part of any process or organism; for it is finished as far as the possibility of change or transformation is concerned. It is this regular and finished part, and this part only, that brain-thinking can represent to itself. You know now what is meant by 'brain-thinking', for it is long since we spoke of it together.

I have not forgotten, said Burgeon. You were teaching me to distinguish the two kinds of 'physical' thinking—an older kind that was physically and sensuously informed, from our kind that is determined by the brain alone, and for that reason can think only *about* the physical.

This kind, continued the Meggid, can grasp only the regular and the finished; because it is itself an end-product. Your brain and your nerves, which are all that this kind uses, are themselves the finished part of your physique—a legacy of the past. It is to other parts that you look, whether you know it or not, for the promise of the future. It is this kind of thinking that seeks and finds regularity; it can do no other; and if it finds, or seems to find, anything else, it is at a loss.

The irregular is the unfinished part—on which the possibility of change and transformation depends, and where change and transformation take their course. All irregularity points the mind towards that part, whether it points from near at hand or still only from afar.

May it not point rather to some deeper law, some other regularity, as yet unapprehended, which further investigation then unveils?

That is a good question. *Then* the pointing is still from far off. Hitherto the brain of man has been impelled by its experience of irregularity to find a more embracing regularity that will account for it—until it has reached a point beyond which it cannot go. Or if it has not yet reached that point, it will do so before long. That ultimate irregularity it classifies, or it will classify, as 'chance'; and that is what you must understand, when you hear men speak of chance as of something that operates in nature alongside the laws they have inferred. You know of the part that was assigned to chance in the science of biology. Some of that irregularity has since been resolved into regularities hitherto unobserved, and, in doing so, the observers have approached nearer to the ultimate irregularity, to the place where change and transformation originate. You have recently learned how the science of physics has been forced even nearer to that point.

Yes, said Burgeon; and it is the point at which some say the search must be abandoned. It would almost seem, from what you say, that they are right; since there is nothing else that they can do.

If it is the love of truth that impels them, and not some other motive, they will do what their predecessors did before them. They will seek in a deeper conformity to law the explanation of what confronts them as 'chance'.

I feel a difficulty looming. Let us suppose that they do so—and even in the science of physics there are those who *are* continuing the endeavour—and let us suppose that they succeed. When the deeper conformity to law has been discovered, it will merely be a new area of regularity won from the shrinking territory of the irregular that still remains. Will not the same problem remain—a little more sharply defined, a little more pinpointed, than it is at present?

It is you, not I, answered the Meggid, who have used the word 'law' as if it were synonymous with regularity. There are other laws of nature beside the regularities which the brain of man has hitherto detected in her. There are the laws on which transformation itself depends. It is to these that they must come at last, whatever further regularities they may unravel on the way, if they seek in the only place that will be left to them—the place where transformation actually occurs. But they will not find in these laws the old clockwork and mathematical regularities to which they have been accustomed, and which they have supposed to be the only laws there are.

'The 'place'—?

You heard me speak, the Meggid interrupted, of a 'deeper' conformity to law. You and I know what shallowness the word 'deep' intends in its customary usage! I once rebuked you for following that usage, and yet now you have repeated the offence! If there were no such anterior and interior place—if *all* that appears to the brain as random and undertermined, could be resolved into those exterior regularities which the brain necessarily seeks, then the world into which it enquires could only be one wherein no transformation is possible, and whereof no evolution is possible.

I testify, said Burgeon, that that is a necessary consequence.

We must go back, said the Meggid, and we need go no farther than last time. I would have you only recall what I said to you then of the transforming agent in nature.

I do recall it. You said men will not recognize that the transforming agent in nature is, in fact, the ultimate energy that stirs in the depths of their own wills. I thought I understood you at the time, but I see that I have not *really* understood until this moment.

Yes, but there was something more, which we also need before I can go farther. I said:

'I am helping you to penetrate the great illusion, which is one with the great tabu. And this is the illusion. The relation between yourself and nature is, not a relation between your body and all else in nature, but the relation between yourself on the one hand and, on the other, your body as at once a part of nature and her epitome.'

This is all-important; nor will you understand it until you have taken hold of it, not as an interesting speculation, but as a part of your daily experience; until it is as obvious to you as waking up in the morning. Yet this alone will not take you very far. The truth that the human body is an epitome of nature was once known to the generality of mankind, and though it has long been lost to their view, they will find that truth again. Even your

Lawrence caught a glimpse of it. But if you would really follow with your mind the *historical* process, which we have only glanced at, you must learn to distinguish farther. If you would faithfully trace the course taken by the mind of man since it first began to apprehend regularity in nature, then you must distinguish, in the domain of nature herself, between the earth and the universe beyond it. It was in that universe beyond, among the stars and planets, that regularity and irregularity were first distinguished. You know that astronomy was the mother of the sciences. It was not until men had transferred the habit of that discernment from the heavens to the earth that they beheld, upon earth too, any 'laws' of nature. And this they could do, because it is out of that universe that the body of the earth has shrunk together. It has shrunk together and gathered into itself the life of the universe, as the seed shrinks together within the parent plant. All its exterior regularities point back to that origin. But the earth is not only a lifeless relic; it is also the living body of mankind, and, permeating the old machine, there is the new life that looks forward to the future. There is the life of human wills, which is so closely involved with their bodies— so much more closely, as you know now, than are their thoughts, their brain-bound thoughts that measure only the regularities come down from the past. You will learn more of this after your death. It is a life that is so far almost wholly unconscious. But it grows a little less so; and that growth will continue. Because it is unconscious, it is not capricious, as the wills of *waking* men are capricious; but neither is it regular, as the legacy of the dead past is regular.

Chance in nature, then, said Burgeon, irreducible chance, is the one token we have so far detected of that sleeping life of will —or rather lives? Technology must seek to calculate even the incalculable—and it can do so only by averaging out the effects of all those unconscious, incalculable wills.

On this the Meggid expressed no opinion. Instead, he continued: It is there alone that true transformation can occur, there that you must look at last—if you are to *study* evolution and not merely to seek new ways of concealing it from yourselves—for the transforming agent. You yourself have puzzled over the essential nature of transformation, finding with your brain that on the one hand there must needs be continuity and, on the other, that if there be continuity, then it is not transformation. Will you not now see that total transformation, *true* transformation, can come only from a transforming agent that transforms itself, and that it is to the 'laws' of that self-transformation that the phenomena said to be governed by chance point your enquiry?

Perhaps, said Burgeon, I may say that I do . . . but I am afflicted by many thoughts . . . this that you have told me . . . this is indeed Existentialism!

You may call it so, and there are some to whom it is well to put it so. To others . . . to Grimwade and Chevalier, perhaps, or others like them, you or another will point out that the law of the Son-Spirit is not the same as the law of the Father-Spirit. And you will be able to remind them why it is that, even in the Christian West, man has hitherto looked in nature, not for the transforming agent, with whom he himself is being made one, but only for the law and rule of the Father; only for 'regularity'. The law of the Father is regular, but the law of the Son becomes only inevitable. Men still seek on earth only those laws of the Father, remaining from the past, which they once sought in the heavens. But tomorrow, whenever the will of the Father is done in earth, as it is in the heavens, it will not be the Father but the Son who does it; and he will do it voluntarily. Whatever names they invent, it is in this direction that those who refuse to abandon it will one day solve the problem of chance.

'What worries me,' said Burgeon, when a few days later he was talking again with Flume, 'is, not the anthropocentricity, but the apparent *geocentricity*.'

He had at last taken the plunge and confided in Flume the whole secret of the Meggid, and Flume had listened in a silence that was neither approving nor disapproving. He was the first person to hear it. Burgeon had felt it an obligation of good faith to communicate to him the Meggid's interpretation of the problem of chance, which they had considered closely together, and that had proved impossible without a full introduction.

'As far as I am concerned,' Flume had said, 'the statement you have just made is a theory. Where it comes from is no concern of mine—not, that is, as a scientist; how it may be for me as a friend is another matter. That is a principle I learned from Popper's *Logic of Scientific Discovery*, before you and I ever began to talk of these things. The question *how it happens* that a new idea occurs to a man, as he says, may be of great interest for empirical psychology; but it is irrelevant to the logical analysis of scientific knowledge. The only questions that arise are: Can it be justified? Does it contradict any other statement we are bound to accept? Can it be tested? How?'

'*Any* understanding,' Burgeon now continued, 'of the relation between our inner and our outer world that is not trivial will be criticized by a materialist or a humanist as anthropocentric. But when you start talking of a relation between the earth and the rest of the universe, your whole frame of reference *is* the outer world. Or so it appears to me. Within that frame of reference we are now being asked to accept—or perhaps I should say I am being asked to accept—that this little planet, in its remote corner, is all-important—is in some sense the centre of all the vast fields of space!'

And now once again it turned out to be Burgeon, the elderly apostle of imagination, who was boggling at a difficulty with which Flume, the youthful physicist, remained comparatively unimpressed.

'Did you say "corner"?' he said. 'You are going out of your way to make difficulties. The centre of the Universe may well turn out to be the point where any observer is stationed.'

'But the *size*, man! The distances!'

'What is size?' asked Flume calmly. 'And who taught you to measure what we call importance by it? In any case, I have long had my doubts about the concept of distance in astronomy—*at least* beyond the confines of the Solar System. You know, this concept of the ψ field is very unsettling. I am not really happy with the practice of measuring distance in light-years, if "measuring" is the right word; and I have long doubted whether it is, in fact, more than a mathematical extrapolation. We talk glibly of light-years—and all the time we know nothing of light itself—except what our wave-and-particle obsession lets through. I begin to suspect that that is precious little. I wonder if Bohm quite realized what he was starting when he pointed back to the Cartesian co-ordinates—that's the posh name for your "corner", you know. He certainly didn't know what he was starting in *me*! And yet,' he went on, speaking more to himself now than to his companion, 'it *can't* be only me! Unsettling I called it—but why aren't they more unsettled? First, it plucked us gently by the sleeve; then, years ago, it whispered

156

plainly to us. Now it is shouting at the top of its voice. A little deafness, you could understand; but why are we *stone* deaf?'

'*What* is shouting at us?'

'Oh, you know well enough. Do you want me to give you my lecture all over again? Why? Why does nobody see it? Didn't your Meggid have any light to throw on *that* question?'

'I wonder—' Burgeon began, and stopped. Flume looked at him enquiringly, but he remained silent for a full half-minute while he pondered. Then, arriving at his decision, he launched into an attempt to impart to Flume all he could summon to mind of the Meggid's long excursus, and his final emphatic warning, on the subject of the great 'tabu'. Flume listened carefully. At the end of it he shook his head.

'All that *describes* the situation,' he said, 'or rather it finds another word for it—the word "tabu". But it doesn't explain it. What I want is an explanation.'

'I thought,' said Burgeon, 'we were both convinced that the explanation is historical—the abolition of the spirit in the adolescence of Western thought—the Fourth Council of—'

'Man alive!' broke in Flume impatiently. 'Can't you see the difference? All that may explain how it came about in the first place. But what I want is an explanation why it *goes on—still* goes on in face of every encouragement to the contrary, in the face of all the evidence! In other words, it explains the error, but not the tabu that preserves it. Did the Meggid say nothing of *why* there is a tabu?'

Burgeon thought of the adversaries, of whom he had as yet said nothing. Should he now?—but he doubted whether he could succeed. In any case, he himself began to fear that some further explanation was needed. After all, the Meggid had spoken to him many times of the adversaries, but only once had he laid that startling emphasis on tabu.

'Then why,' said Flume, breaking in on his reflections, 'don't you ask him?'

'If I am given the opportunity,' Burgeon answered, 'I will do so.' He spoke slowly, because he was thinking, as well, of two other questions he had long been waiting to ask. Now perhaps would be the time.

We shall conclude with the best account we can give of the answers that the Meggid shortly afterwards vouchsafed to all three questions.

THIRTEEN

In the course of your own reflections (it is the Meggid speaking) it was through the problem of behaviour, and the transformation of character, that you first became able to penetrate at all deeply into the nature of transformation itself. To a mind preoccupied in depth, as yours was, with the relation between law and morality I was able to reveal the two adversaries and the parts they play.

If you would understand, other than superficially, the history of man and of the earth on which his body dwells, you must know that it proceeded in the same order. A point came in it, when he had to discover the difference between the morality of regulation and the morality of self-transformation through death and rebirth. This last, as you well know, is an interior event; and it is interior, not only to the race as a whole, but to each individual man. Therefore it required millennia of preparation, even to— how shall I put it to you?—even to clear the stage for it. The consciousness of individual man had first to be sheltered, cut off from the life of nature hitherto pulsing through it. It was indeed by that means that he *became* individual man. There followed the time when he could be faced with the problem and shown the way to rebirth. We have spoken of it together. You know how little, save here and there, he has as yet found that way. Yet already the time of his shelter is drawing to a close; and he is beginning to rediscover his one-ness with the earth, his one-ness with nature. But even now he has hardly begun to discover what follows: that the transformation of nature through death and rebirth, and therefore the continued *life* of the earth, is now the body of which his own self-transformation is the soul.

Because of all that has passed between us already I may thus put the greatest things into the smallest compass. Nor need I repeat what you have heard from me already of the adversaries— how *they* seek, not transformation but either continuity or substitution. We have spoken little as yet of good and evil. If you are wise, you will not think of the adversaries as evil. Not they, but what they *do*, if man himself fails to prevent it, is evil. They are not evil, because it is only in the activity of preventing them that man achieves freedom: the freedom without which his transformation would not be self-transformation. And did you not discover for yourself that, in the last resort, there can be no transformation, no *true* transformation—true because exempt alike from continuity and from substitution—that is not self-transformation?

To avert substitution there must be persistence; to avert continuity there must be discontinuity, that is to say there must be destruction of the old form. When men cease to look only for continuity they will find that there is this destruction of the form, this momentary return to chaos, in every common seed in the article of its germination.

My brothers are saying, said Burgeon now, that the form of the new plant is remembered or imitated or decoded in some way from the form of the old. Is it because they are so determined to find a continuity that is not there that they do not realize how anthropomorphic their notions become?

It was indeed the false Preserver, continued the Meggid, who first led them to their doctrine of the conservation of matter, and then led them to idolize it. They will discover—and it may be soon—that that is not a law of universal application. This destruction, this destruction which is the precondition of every transformation—where must it be most absolute? Where transformation is most absolute. Within man himself. Your brothers in the West will learn, indeed they are beginning to suspect already, that within each one of them, deep-hidden and hitherto unconscious, there lives a fury of destructive force, beside which the destructive forces in nature grow pale.

What they ordinarily call self-knowledge is no more than a lifeless network of memory-thoughts spun about the self, as the hypotheses of science are spun about the self of nature. But when they penetrate beneath the lifeless memory-thoughts which the brain reflects; when they begin to reach behind the network to the living thought, which is at the same time the source of life in nature, when consciousness begins to penetrate the sleeping human will itself, then indeed the hitherto unconscious impulse to blot out the given material form breaks through into actual instinct. It becomes the instinct to destroy *all* form, to spread abroad in the world around them the chaos they have dimly begun to divine within themselves. You once consulted me about a faint reverberation in modern adolescence of this abysmal *Schadenfreude*. But your generation knows it well already from more disastrous manifestations.

This destructive impulse and this chaos mankind has long unconsciously feared. And that fear, if you will receive it, is the true origin of materialism. It is founded in fear. The fear of what you will find becomes the fear to look, the fear to look becomes the wish that it may be impossible to look, and from that unconscious wish springs the doctrine of the conservation of matter and energy which, if it were wholly true, would indeed render it impossible to look behind those lifeless memory-thoughts that are a mere mirror to reflect alike the surface of nature and the surface of self.

But it is not wholly true. It is not true within the human being himself. There, in his metabolism, matter is not conserved; it is destroyed and re-created. And it is from there that *his* life, and with it *his* morality, must begin to inform nature, to inform the earth itself. This he can only do by pouring his morality into the heart and centre of destruction that he carries within himself.

I, too, feel afraid, stammered Burgeon.

You are all afraid, said the Meggid gravely. Afraid even to *look* into that terrible heart and centre. It is well that some in the West at least begin to be dimly aware that there *is* this abiding fear, this haunting anxiety, at the root of their being.

There was a pause.

But this task, said Burgeon at last—this 'pouring' of which you speak—men have not even remotely begun on it! The farthest they get when they do begin to penetrate, when they see that there are depths below the surface of the brain-thoughts, into which materialism would not have them look . . . the farthest they get . . . there was a man—about him, too, I once consulted you—who taught the exact opposite of what you are saying: not that morality must enter into nature, but rather that nature must enter into morality.

He was bewildered, came the answer, by the weight of what he divined. Is it surprising? Yet I recall how, even before you found me, *you* had divined his bewilderment. It was his truth, not his error, that you had failed to see: the truth that nature on the one hand and human morality on the other are not, as men think, divided by an impassable gulf, but, in the depths from which all transformation springs, are one.

But have I answered your question? Have I at least shown you why I used the word? Tabu is moral shock. Do you now under-stand a little both the origin and the violence of the great tabu of which I spoke?

In the 'silence' that followed Burgeon became aware that the Meggid had not yet left him. Master, he said at last, using the word for the first time, there is another question I would ask, if it is permitted. And the question is this: How is it that *I* am made the recipient of this wide volume of awareness, this weight of knowledge? For this last adventure that you bade—a rabbit without mathematics; and for the rest, a soul without courage or nearly so!

It was one of those rare occasions on which, if he had been asked for his impression, he would have been almost obliged to say that the Meggid 'smiled', as he replied:

Have you supposed that you are the only one? There are others, whom you will find, if you have not done so already. But if you ask why *you* are one of the few—then there are a few positive, and many negative reasons. A gardener who is to plant a seed difficult of growth must take both kinds into consideration. He knows that it will need, if it is to survive, not only favourable soil but, even more, a sheltered spot. How often, with a regretful shake of the head, he will abandon the richer soil in the exposed position for the poorer but well-screened plot! You have led what is for this age a sheltered life. The two holocausts have touched you comparatively lightly, the reigns of terror not at all. Reflect, too, on the millions whom these have battered or dam-aged or unavoidably engrossed in feverish activity, and on those other millions whom they have removed altogether from the earth. Many among them would have been reached before you. The area of our choice at present is not so wide. As to any positive reasons—it is not a matter to which you need give much attention.

I am answered, Master; but I have yet one more question. It is a question I have wished to put before. Almost from the beginning I have been minded to ask it. But—why, I do not know—though there is the old story of Cupid and Psyche—I have hitherto refrained. It is: Who are *you*? You told me once, of your own accord, that you were a servant of Michael. But I think that cannot be the whole answer. And indeed I recall that Karo's Maggid on different occasions gave more than one answer to the same question.

I would have thought, said the voice that was no voice, that I had answered that already. But I will repeat a portion of what I said. The thoughts you think all day are memory-thoughts. Your brain reflects, as a mirror does, the world that is delivered to it by the senses, and your thoughts are the remainder-shadows which memory makes from those reflected images. It is behind that mirror that the forces of destruction are concealed, of which I have spoken; and the mirror is indeed your protection from them. If, instead of remaining content with looking on the reflections and thinking with the shadows that memory makes of them, a man breaks through the mirror to look behind it, he encounters, it is true, the forces of destruction. But not them alone. For the centre of destruction is also the centre of rebirth. In that heart and centre dwells the inner word. And that, too, is encountered.

You are one of those who have at least peeped behind the mirror. And what you have found there so far is thought. But these thoughts are other than your memory-thoughts, of which they are none the less the source and origin. For these are the creative thoughts themselves. They are the substance, not only of the world which brain and sense reflect, but also of sense and brain themselves; they are nothing remembered, because they are one with the life itself that supports and enables the act of memory. Therefore it is that, when you experience them at all, you cannot experience them—as you do the memory-thoughts —as being 'your own' because spun from your brain. They own an objectivity which in terms of everyday life you can better compare with perceiving than with thinking. And yet they are indeed your own in the deepest sense of all, because, unlike the memory-thoughts, they are also your substance and your life; so that to perceive them is verily to perceive the spirit within you in the act of creating.

How, then, does a man experience them? Only by a hearing that is at the same time a speaking. Only as if they were at the same time communicated by another and uttered by himself. Are you answered? Have you not yet understood? Yes. I am indeed a servant of Michael; but because I am spirit without

162

body I may also truly say that I am all those wherein I am contained, I am all that speaks through me. Men have called me by many names; Batkhol, Daimon, Khochmah, and many more. But that was long ago. Men have called me also *Sophia*. Once I was the ancestral voice of the Father-wisdom, the *theosophia* that spoke inarticulately through blood and instinct, but spoke articulately only in the mysteries and through the sibyls, the prophets, the masters. But at the turning-point of time, by that central death and rebirth which was the transformation of transformations, by the open mystery of Golgotha, I was myself transformed. I am that *anthroposophia* who, by whatsoever communications howsoever imparted she shall first have been evoked, is the voice of each one's mind speaking from the depths within himself.

The voice fell silent.

And his task when he has heard it? came the anxious question. What then, oh, what then shall he do?

Twice, answered the gentle but inexorable voice, twice now you have called me 'Master'. But what you shall do shall be taught you not by me, neither by my masters. You may only receive it direct from the Master of my masters; who is also their humble servant, as each one of them also is mine; as you—if your 'doing' should be only a writing—will strive to be your reader's, and as

I am

yours.